# Human Frailties

# Richard Gordon

# Human Frailties

SINCLAIR-STEVENSON

First published in Great Britain in 1995
by Sinclair-Stevenson
an imprint of Reed Consumer Books Ltd
Michelin House, 81 Fulham Road, London SW3 6RB
and Auckland, Melbourne, Singapore and Toronto

A CIP catalogue record for this book
is available at the British Library
ISBN 1 85619 454 X

Typeset by CentraCet Limited, Cambridge
Printed and bound in Great Britain
by Clays Ltd, St Ives PLC

To
Jo
*Again*

Our frailties are invincible, our virtues barren;
the battle goes sore against us to
the going down of the sun.

Robert Louis Stevenson
*Pluvis et Umbra*

# Contents

# ONE

# Basic Instincts

'Lord, what fools these mortals be!' Never was a truer word spoken in genius.

We intelligent humans, who express the ultimate in biological development – who browse through bookshops, idly opening the covers, deciding whether their contents are worth spending money on – may feel offended that we are nonetheless impelled by ten fundamental instincts:

- 1 To stay alive.
- 2 To eat.
- 3 To quench our thirst.
- 4 To keep warm.
- 5 To go to the loo.
- 6 To stay out of harm's way.
- 7 To rest after exertion.
- 8 To exert ourselves after rest.
- 9 To enjoy orgasms.
- 10 To keep our self-esteem.

In 1908, William McDougall from Manchester, later an enthusiastic professor of psychology at Harvard, was so stimulated by Darwin's depiction of man – as no better than a haughty animal – that he increased our brutish instincts to eighteen. The professor next neatly yoked our impulses to our emotions. Our prudent instinct for taking flight was accompanied by the feeling of quivering fear. A display of aggression – always enjoyable – was masked with the emotion of anger. Our sense of curiosity usefully contrived both the discovery of food and the avoidance of prowling enemies. Feelings of disgust ensured our safe recoil against eating something nasty and noxious.

The notion of our doing everything because we could not help it was so appealing, in the face of our everyday behaviour, that the list of instincts was quickly expanded by his fellow psychologists to 5,000.

This was over-optimistic.

Many of these 5,000 'instincts' were only reflexes. A reflex is a stimulus to a sense organ which excites an inward-going nerve, which excites an outward-going nerve to activate a muscle. Cross your legs, tap briskly below your kneecap with the spine of this book, and see for yourself. Breathing, coughing, colic, blinking, laughing from tickling, erections, a racing pulse: all are reflexes.

Such activities were first conceived by René Descartes, and are comparable to the automatic windscreen-wiping, headlight-flashing and acceleration of another conception of ourselves: *l'homme-machine*. Descartes first drove this rattling model recklessly through the philosophical countryside in 1662. The brain was its engine, the mysterious little pineal gland tucked into the brain's rear was its sparking-plug, the body's nerves were the transmission and big end; it ran on a tankful of super 'animal spirits' and the maker's name was God, to whom it was returnable after use.

Sigmund Freud, whose ghost still shrieks from the shuddery untrodden regions of the mind, in 1923 bundled the instincts into one and created the Id. This is easiest conceived as an untrained savage Rottweiler, kept on the lead by the streetwise Ego, and continually frightening the life out of the fussily attendant Super-ego.

Such are the flatteringly learned, if suspiciously varied, explanations of why the male and female creations that God effected so effortlessly are not infallibly responsible for what they do.

In the 1930s, zoologists like Konrad Lorenz began seeking instruction about human behaviour from the instinctive activity of animals. This is misleading, however fascinating. For example, the female digger-wasp emerges from the ground in the springtime and within a few weeks mates, digs out a nest of separated cells, hunts and kills caterpillars to provision it, lays her eggs, seals up the cells and dies. She could have learned nothing of this complex race-perpetuative behaviour from her parents, both of which perished the summer before she was born.

But this performance is undeviating, like that of the male stickleback who attacks an intruding male stickleback under the specific stimulus of the other stickleback's red belly. Animals' instinctive courtship rituals – such as the inflation of the proboscis and the roaring of the elephant seal, the post-coital devouring of the male by the female scorpion, the splashy water dancing of the great crested grebe – however spectacular, are surpassed by the infinitely variable, complicated and subtle means that humans employ to get themselves into bed together.

The brain itself, Hamlet's seat of 'capability and god-like reason', was discovered by physiologists to be a telephone exchange, but it is now seen as a thick soup of electrically charged chemicals. In this pensive *velouté* our feelings bubble and plop up from the hippocampus, which is a tiny morsel lying at the bottom of the brain-pan, and which creates and expresses our emotions, organises our memory and imparts the flavour of life.

Our instincts become complicated through our jumpiness at possibly failing to achieve these ten compelling needs. We try to distance such a disaster as far as possible. We do not normally fulfil Instinct No. 2 by arriving at a party and grabbing all the sandwiches and little sausages. Nor do we satisfy Instinct No. 6 by staying safely all day in bed. Nor is No. 9 achieved by men continually committing rape upon women exhibiting rabid nymphomania; nor No. 10 by telling everybody how lovely we are – well, not always. Instead, we stick to our boring jobs and save up against a hungry day; we drive carefully and buy insurance; we marry when this convenience reasonably presents itself; and we strive for status in our own little world, whether this revolves daily in best circles or in a ring of criminals.

'I can calculate the motions of the heavenly bodies, but not the madness of people,' Isaac Newton observed forlornly in 1720, while his country was losing its gravity in the South Sea Bubble (he lost £20,000). The earth offers endless and rich opportunities for man's unexpected, irrational, and lunatic behaviour. These are particularly alarming and unexpected when we are doing anything all together. Like ants and bees, which cannot exist outside a community, humans are fundamentally gregarious. Oscar Wilde put it feelingly: 'The brotherhood of man is not a mere poet's dream: it is a most depressing and humiliating reality.'

'Have you ever seen, in some wood, on a sunny quiet day, a cloud of flying midges – thousands of them – hovering, apparently motionless, in a sunbeam? . . . Yes? Well, did you ever see the whole flight – each mite apparently preserving its distance from all the others – suddenly move, say, three feet, to one side or the other? Well, *what made them do that*? A breeze? I said a *quiet* day. But try to recall – did you ever see them move directly back again in the same unison? Well, what made

4

them do *that*? Great human mass movements are slower of inception but much more effective.'

This quotation came after the slaughterhouse stampede of the Great War and the mass financial foolishness of the Great Crash, in the preface to the 1932 edition of a book by Charles Mackay, LL D Glasgow.

Mackay was born in Perth in 1814, and after his mother's death during his infancy was reared by his nurse Grace Stuart in a lonely house beside the Firth of Forth. He was schooled in Brussels, wrote French, became secretary to a Liège ironmaster, edited the Glasgow *Argus*, covered the American Civil War for *The Times*, was the father of the novelist Marie Corelli, died on Christmas Eve 1889, and lies in the company of Thackeray and Trollope at Kensal Green in west London. He was also a songwriter, whose 'Cheer, Boys! Cheer!' and 'There's a Good Time Coming' both sold half a million. His prose includes *The Scenery and Poetry of the English Lakes*, *Life and Liberty in America*, and *The Poetry and Humour of the Scottish Language*.

In 1841, he wrote the three-volume *Extraordinary Popular Delusions and the Madness of Crowds*. That book is the chillingly topical inspiration for this one.

# TWO

# Fools and their Money

What an unthinkingly maligned article is money! Money is the flowing currency of human anxiety lest our ten instinctive impulses – listed in the first chapter – might possibly go unsatisfied. Money is our ringing shield against being overwhelmed one awful day by hunger and thirst. It is the necessary coin for achieving even the purest orgasms – you cannot readily marry unless you can afford to.

Money forges easily into the adjustable pedestal of our self-esteem. Monks and unsuccessful artists and tramps think themselves the better for having no money at all. The affluent can buy importance by cluttering themselves with items like Rolls-Royces and jewels which forcefully express it. For most of us, who never have quite enough of it, money affords the pleasant paradox of contempt for those with a lot of it. No wonder that people like money so much that its lack, as Mark Twain said, is the root of all evil.

Money moves only as the mind moves. The bossy science of economics is thus only a branch of psychology. Freud and Keynes hold hands across the pecuniary sufferer's couch.

The simple Scroogian desire for money by itself, the miser's ill-nourished lifestyle, is a harmless solitary hobby like stamp-collecting. The desire for what money can bring propels humans into disaster at a rate which leaves the Gadarene swine standing at the post.

Here are some of man's adventures in his resolute quest for fool's gold.

### Mississippi Dreamboat

The Place Vendôme in Paris today has Napoleon in the middle, dressed up as Caesar atop 1,200 melted-down cannon captured at Austerlitz, viewing the Rue de Rivoli, with the Ritz on one side, the Opéra behind up the Rue de la Paix, and to his left Drouant's agreeable fish restaurant where they yearly award the Prix Goncourt.

In 1717, a third of this fashionable *quartier* was owned by John Law from Edinburgh, the son of a goldsmith and banker who lived on sweeping estates by the Firth of Forth. By then, John Law owned several other valuable pieces of Paris, a dozen rural châteaux, and the French Banque Générale. In 1694, he had killed a man: Edward 'Beau' Wilson, a London swell who lived by means mysterious even to his intimates.

Law in London was then aged twenty-three, handsome – though, like all its lucky survivors, scarred by the smallpox – tall, vain, a dandy, a mathematical prodigy, an earnest gambler, and like James Boswell, who followed him a century later on 'the noblest prospect which a Scotchman ever sees', the high road to England, he was avid for women. Law had affronted Beau Wilson over one Elizabeth (she later did well, becoming Countess of Orkney), was challenged to a duel and shot him. He was found guilty of murder, but his death sentence for sexual rivalry was sportingly commuted to a fine for manslaughter. Wilson's family angrily appealed and Law was locked in the King's Bench prison, but he escaped and fled to

Amsterdam, where he continued his studies of political economy.

In self-exile through his failure to win a royal pardon, Law supported himself for fifteen years by gambling his way round Europe. He ingratiated himself with a fellow-gamester, the Duc d'Orléans, who in 1715 became Regent for the seven-year-old King Louis XV. With a little help from such friends at court, on 20 May 1716 Law established the Banque Générale, the first bank ever to be founded in France. It rested on 1,200 shares of 5,000 *livres*, and it issued its own banknotes — sixty million *livres* of them, redeemable for a given weight of hard cash and trustworthily accepted in payment for taxes.

A year after founding the bank, Law formed the Compagnie de la Louisiane ou d'Occident to exploit the Mississippi basin, which everyone knew was bursting with precious metals. The Company had concessions to coin Mississippi currency, collect American taxes and run the tobacco monopoly. A year after that, the Banque Générale became the Banque Royale, your money clearly and safely backed by the King. The next year, Law's Louisiana Company took over India and China. There was no stopping him.

The French economy on Law's arrival in Paris had been shattered by the extravagance of Louis XIV. The national debt was 3,000 million *livres*, on which the government could raise only a minuscule 0.001 per cent to pay interest to its bondholders. It seemed reasonable to the Duc d'Orléans and to everyone else that so capable a Scotsman should become Comptroller-general of Finances. His job was to take over the French mint, issue the French coinage, run the French tax-farming and pay off the French national debt.

Everyone now wanted a piece of Law's banks and companies. They besieged his house in the Rue de Quincampoix, which is a narrow street running north from the Rue de Rivoli. Limbs and heads were broken daily in the crush to invest. The local cobbler with a street-stall quit his last, profitably to furnish the acquisitive mob with quills and writing-paper. The local hunchback did nicely leasing his hump for a desk. The neighbourhood property values soared and John Law quit for the Place Vendôme, to be followed by even bigger crowds and diversionary tents providing food, drink and roulette.

Over a quarter-million provincials stormed Paris to press money into Law's hands. They caused the price of beds, nourishment and smart attire to shoot up, and created the city's enduring traffic jams. For thirty thousand moneyed and noble and touristic Britons, springtime in Paris that year of 1719 was enhanced with burgeoning investment. Their Ambassador, the Earl of Stair (who had got the Old Pretender expelled from Paris), had already been showered with letters from fellow Scots begging him to handle their investments. He now dispatched to London his concern at the King's subjects leaping the Channel with the nation's capital in their saddle-bags.

Law was the saviour of France. He needed a troop of horse to clear a way for his carriage through the open-mouthed enthusiasm of his wonderstruck beneficiaries. He soared in the perfumed heavens of Paris society, mobbed in every salon by angelic females seeking a piece of his financial action. 'Law is so run after that he has no rest day or night,' wrote the Regent's mother. 'A duchess kissed his hands before everyone, and if duchesses kiss his hands, what parts of him won't the other ladies salute?'

This Parisian midsummer madness was excited by Law's promising 120 per cent profit on his Mississippi shares. These nominally went for 500 *livres* each, but if you bought them with the now devalued *billets d'état* they cost only 100. In the scramble, the price could rise 20 per cent between meals. It hit 10,000 *livres*, making a profit of 500,000 *livres* for a coachman sent by a trustful master to sell 250 shares which that breakfast-time were standing at only 8,000. Cooks and cookmaids enjoyed affluence indistinguishable from their employers'. A humble M. André sought to improve his family socially by paying the 33-year-old Marquis d'Oyse 100,000 crowns down, then 20,000 *livres* a year, until he married the marquis's three-year-old daughter when she turned twelve.

Everybody bought Law's shares with paper money, which was obligingly issued by Law's bank. In 1720, the Prince de Conti returned three wagonloads of this paper – as he was entitled to – for repayment in gold and silver. But under pressure from the alarmed Law, the Regent made the Prince send two-thirds of the specie back. Then everybody got the same idea as the Prince. Stockjobber M. Vermalet loaded a farm cart with a million *livres* of gold and silver coins, covered them with cow dung, donned a smock and clopped off to Belgium. This widespread and reasonable desire to change paper into money was disastrous. There was hard cash enough only to cast the metal of a magnet for panic. Coin was devalued by five per cent, next by ten per cent, and in February 1720 near abolished altogether. No Frenchman was allowed to possess more than 500 *livres* in cash, nor to put his money into gold plate and jewellery, and informers inciting a search-warrant and the arrival of the police got half the spoils. This brought threatened revolution.

Law had casually but ceremoniously become a Catholic to get his job of Comptroller, but his religious sincerity seemed clear to Lord Stair: the convert had established an Inquisition, to enforce his faith in the transubstantiation of gold into paper. As a national encouragement, 6,000 men sleeping rough in Paris were rounded up, clothed, and paraded with picks and shovels preparatory to their transportation to dig up the wealth of the Mississippi, but luckily most of them escaped, sold their tools, spent the money on drink and went back to their doorsteps.

In June, Law's devalued banknotes made an official bonfire outside the Hôtel de Ville, and new ones were issued. These were reliably exchangeable at the Banque Royale for silver or, when they quickly ran out of it, copper. Such was the enthusiasm for this transaction that customers were regularly crushed to death in the bank's doors: once, fifteen in a day, and the military who were called in to restore order shot dead a few more. The Banque went bust, the Mississippi shares were worthless. M. André's daughter's marriage was off, though the Marquis d'Oyse kept the 100,000 crowns.

Law's carriage was now stoned in the streets, his family attacked, his life endangered, and the safety of his house required a resident company of the Regent's Swiss guards. Law slipped away from France that Christmas and died in Venice in the spring nine years later. In 1719, he had at last been pardoned for his shooting Beau Wilson. In 1720, the world was clamouring to have him hanged. The charge was even shakier than defending yourself in a duel. John Law was only an accomplice of an everlasting human frailty: of slipping any conveniently dangling silken noose round its own neck.

### The South Sea Bubble

The South Sea Bubble, which has bounced along British history, sparkled amid the lather of the Mississippi Scheme. It was the age of too much money chasing too few realities.

In 1717, the thinking Englishman was loaded.

11

'During the interval between the Restoration and the Revolution the riches of the nation had been rapidly increasing,' Lord Macaulay was recalling pleasantly in the middle of the nineteenth century. 'Thousands of busy men found every Christmas that, after the expenses of the year's housekeeping had been defrayed out of the year's income, a surplus remained; and how that surplus was to be employed was a question of some difficulty.'

About the same time, economist Walter Bagehot was noting in *Lombard Street* the contemporary trend that 'an Englishman – a modern Englishman at least – assumes as a first principle that he ought to be able to "put his money into something safe that will yield 5 per cent"'. But as Macaulay continued recollecting: 'In the seventeenth century, a lawyer, a physician, a retired merchant, who had saved some thousands, and who wished to place them safely and profitably, was often greatly embarrassed.'

Land then was scarce and static. Lending to men, or as 'bottomry' on ships, was unduly risky. You could put your cash into East India Company stock, if you could get your hands on any. Otherwise, like Alexander Pope's father, you could lock it all in a strong-box and retire to the country, there opening up now and then for running expenses.

It is a human weakness that the faster you accumulate your savings, the faster the losing of them you are prepared to risk. 'The natural effect of this state of things', saw Macaulay, 'was that a crowd of projectors, ingenious and absurd, honest and knavish, employed themselves in devising new schemes for the employment of capital.' In 1688, the 'stockjobber' was first heard of in London. Within five years, these jobbers had conjured a crowd of companies promising immense profits – the Lutestring Company, the Pearl Fishery Company, the Diving Company, to surface sunken treasure in Cyclops-eyed suits of armour with air-pipes, the Royal Academies Company for educating gentlemen – all of which shortly returned to the nothingness from which they were created.

In 1711, an interesting new investment opportunity presented itself. The South Sea Company was founded by Robert Harley, Chancellor of the Exchequer. It was the year that he was stabbed with a penknife by a Frenchman, and was made the Earl of Oxford when he recovered. The Company had the monopoly of trade with the Pacific and South America; its ships would round the Horn laden with English broadcloth and cotton shirts and ironmongery, then sail homeward-bound heavy with ingots from the mines of Potosi-la-Paz. It would be grossly overpaid for these exported goods by the simple natives of South America. Everybody knew that gold and silver was oozing from Peru and Mexico as inexhaustibly as winter mud from the English shires.

The idea was so sound that the Company took over part of the British national debt, in return for being paid interest at 6 per cent, which the Government raised by taxing wine, silks, tobacco, and the whalebones for ladies' stays. But the King of Spain awkwardly refused to let English traders anywhere near his American colonies, though he granted them (for a quarter of the profits) the dispatch of one ship a year, and the supplying of negro slaves for thirty years.

This rebuff did not affect English enthusiasm for the South Sea Company. In 1718, George I became its Governor. In 1720, the Company took the bull market by the horns and paid £7.5 million for the rest of the £52 million national debt. The idea was to entice Englishmen to swap their stodgy Government annuities for exciting South Sea stock. As this stock enjoyed a premium as high as its optimism, the deal would be a smart one for the Company, particularly as the Government would pay it £1.5 million a year interest as well. The Bank of England

13

thought the scheme splendid – so emphatically that it made its own bid for the national debt, but luckily for itself was scorned.

On 12 April 1720, a million South Sea shares were on offer, but two million were wanted by the public. A second million was marketed, and consumed between the morning loaf and midday beef. Five million shares ended up in fingers eager and grateful. Two-thirds of the Government's annuity-holders tumbled to convert, to be rewarded by seeing their South Sea stock rise from 130 to 890 by June 1720, and to 1,000 by July. Frenchmen had been switching from Mississippi into South Sea, Exchange Alley and Cornhill held crowds like the Rue de Quincampoix and the Place Vendôme, with encouragement spreading among them from such news that the King of Spain had just accepted Gibraltar in exchange for all his ports in Peru.

> Statesmen and patriot ply alike the stocks,
> Peeress and butler share alike the box;
> And judges job, and bishops bite the town,
> And mighty dukes pack cards for half-a-crown:
> See Britain sunk in Lucre's sordid charms,

wrote the poet whose father was safely in the country with his money in a chest.

Meanwhile, the stockjobbers returned to their 1688 tricks. Companies were founded, that 1720 summer, of such ingenious uselessness that many must have been chucklesome hoaxes. Had they proved successful, they would have made fresh water from the sea, founded hostels for bastards, imported large jackasses from Spain, perpetuated perpetual motion, fished for whales off Greenland, improved Flint, paved London, drained the Fens, traded in hair, furnished funerals nationwide, beautified soap, bettered the beer, recreated planks from sawdust, insured horses and servants, extracted silver from lead, fattened hogs, rebuilt parsonages, and revolutionised war with square cannon-balls. An economic cliché from the Bubble days is the company 'for carrying on an undertaking of great advantage, but nobody to know what it is', for which a thousand punters deposited two guineas on a £100 share in the morning, and in the afternoon the promoter was on his way to Amsterdam.

Grand names reassuringly sponsored these wild schemes, from the Prince of Wales down (he collected £40,000), thus founding a stockjobbing tradition. Gentlemen bought shares in their taverns, ladies at their milliners – in the excitement no one cared what their investment was for, because everyone knew that shares in anything rose, then you sold them at a profit. Simple.

Why, you could make ten per cent by walking from one end of Exchange Alley to the other. Everybody knew that this was the right thing to do, because everybody else was doing it. 'When the rest of the world are mad, we must imitate them in some measure,' the man who owned Martin's bank excused himself feebly at the time. When the Lords Justices, sitting in the Privy Council, dissolved eighty-six of these soapsud ventures on 12 July, they were considered killjoys.

In August, South Sea stock fell steadily to 700. Sanctimonious Dissenter Sir John Blunt, the South Sea chairman, decided to call a shareholders' meeting. The hall was packed, the City streets choked, the shares went down to 640. In September they reached 400, in October they were back at 130. Families were beggared, squires ruined, clergymen straitened, moneylenders in flight. The Sword-blade Company, which was the South Sea's bank, shut the till.

The spurned Bank of England generously tried propping up South Sea shares by raising a loan, but the effort lasted only a morning. Avarice turned to anger. The King

**15**

hastened home from Hanover. Parliament was recalled, to uncover that the Company had cooked the books and bribed government ministers. Black Rod took charge of five directors, including Gibbon's grandfather. The Chancellor of the Exchequer, James Aislabie, was found guilty of 'notorious, dangerous and infamous corruptions', and magnificently sent to the Tower. The chairman's brother Charles cut his throat. The Company's missing treasurer, John Knight, had £2,000 put on his head by royal proclamation, but escaped to Liège. The Duchy of Brabant was still snootily refusing to extradite him, when he escaped from Antwerp citadel to make a fortune in Paris.

Lord Molesworth, in the House of Lords, wanted the directors sewn into sacks and thrown into the Thames. George I's favourite, the 48-year-old statesman Earl Stanhope, spoke there so vehemently against a reflection upon his own involvement that he had a stroke, was cupped, was let blood the next morning, but died by nightfall. Bookseller Thomas Guy did so well from selling stock at the right time that he had £18,793 idle to pay for building Guy's Hospital.

The strongest voice in Parliament against the South Sea scheme had been Robert Walpole's: 'It would hold out a dangerous lure to decoy the unwary to their ruin, by making them part with the earnings of their labour for a prospect of imaginary wealth . . . The great principle of the project was an evil of first-rate magnitude; it was to raise artificially the value of the stock, by exciting and keeping up a general infatuation, and by promising dividends out of funds which could never be adequate for the purpose.' As he punned about the War of Jenkins's Ear, the country rang the bells all summer, to wring their empty hands in November.

Never send to know for whom the bells of credulity ring: they ring for thee.

## The Great Crash

The Great Fire of London, the Great Plague, Pompeii, and the Flood, were comparable classic disasters to the collapse of Wall Street on Thursday, 25 October 1929.

The New York stock market had been rising all summer. Unlike the sweltering temperature outside, it had no foreseeable top. Like Paris in 1719 and London in 1720, to become rich all you needed to do was to buy stocks. You did not even need the money. Increasingly throughout the 1920s, investors were borrowing it avidly from equally zealous stockbrokers. You put up half the cost of your shares, and on the rest you paid loan interest of five per cent. Nearer to the Crash this rate rose, through popular demand for such an admirable service, to twelve per cent. This was no worry when you opened your paper each morning to find your loan shrinking to a gratifying and sometimes ridiculous fraction of your new wealth, which was acquired by doing absolutely nothing, and without even such commonplace tediums of possession as having to feed it, or paint it, or insure it, or put it somewhere.

Everyone was thus buying stocks 'on margin'. Everyone of the commercially chattering classes was swapping tips: patients with their doctors and nurses, actors and poets with their agents, millionaires to their valets, chauffeurs to cops. Housewives were becoming as intensely interested in share values as in social ones. Western cowboys were wiring orders to join the national rodeo. Everyone wanted to become rich, but without grasping the mechanism by which this would so happily happen. New companies and investment trusts were established lavishly, to give ever enterprising Americans something untroublesome to put their borrowed money into. These companies were themselves founded on borrowed cash, and through complicated systems of diversification somehow managed to invest heavily in themselves.

In 1929, there were 1,548,707 punters on Wall Street, over half a million of them playing 'on margin' by borrowing $7 billion a month. Everything was 'hunky-dory', as they were saying. On the Friday before Black Thursday, the *New York Times*' industrial shares average, shining as reliably as the sun high in the Manhattan sky all summer, set for the night down 7 points. On the Saturday, it was down 12. On the Wednesday, it had dropped 31, from 415 to 384. On that Thursday morning it vanished. Into the whirlwind swirled 12,894,650 shares, and nobody wanted to sweep them up. Their owners were illuminated in a lightning-flash that whatever people wanted to sell, for which there were no buyers, was worthless. All they had left was a debt.

Walter Bagehot explained in *Lombard Street* of 1873:

> At first, incipient panic amounts to a kind of vague conversation: Is A. B. as good as he used to be? Has not C. D. lost money? and a thousand such questions. A hundred people are talked about, and a thousand think, 'Am I talked about, or am I not?' 'Is my credit as good as it used to be, or is it less?' And every day, as a panic grows, this floating suspicion becomes both more intense and more diffused; it attacks more persons, and attacks them all more virulently than at first. All men of experience, therefore, try to 'strengthen themselves', as it is called, in the early stage of a panic; they borrow money while they can ... And if the merchant be a regular customer, a banker does not like to refuse, because if he does he will be said, or may be said, to be in want of money, and so may attract the panic to himself.

Those were more leisurely days even for panics. In 1929, something had to be done at once. At Thursday noon, a meeting of bankers in the J. P. Morgan offices

18

declared that they were putting up money to save the stock market. The vice-president of the Stock Exchange descended like vice-God on to the trading floor and ceremoniously bought a sheaf of steel shares. The trading day closed with the *Times*' index off only 12. But that was because during the afternoon smarter people with a bag of ready money could refill it with shares lying cheap in the dirt.

Everybody calmed down over the weekend. On Monday 28 October, the index fell 49 points, and another 2,250,000 shares went begging. On Tuesday, it fell 43, with 16,410,000 shares thrown to the winds. The vice-president of the Stock Exchange was perceived to be no god, but a boy on a burning deck. The ticker-tape chattering out the stock prices became so clogged with disastrous news that it ran two and a half hours late. You could not even reach for a stiff drink, because for nearly ten years they had all been prohibited.

In 1925, there had been a minatory preview in Florida, which everybody was then buying up on a ten per cent deposit, and watching delightedly the bounding land values as desirable building plots changed hands, until a real hurricane in the autumn of 1926 precipitated the realisation that all each landlord owned was an unsaleable chunk of swamp.

The Stock Exchange wondered nervously whether to halt the crash with the magnificently simple stroke of closing down. It had in the one of 1873, after the railroad swindle. But it decided to take extra holidays instead. Stockbrokers were believed to be lining the Wall Street window-ledges, preparatory to hurling themselves upon the sidewalks, but the only one so observed with hearty approbation by the crowds of investors cramming the financial district was a man come to repair the roof.

The financial wizards of America were flabbergasted. They could not understand why the Crash had happened.

They could not understand why it ever *should* have happened. Further, they did not even believe that it had happened. Less than a year before, the former President, Calvin Coolidge, was complimenting Congress on overseeing a state of the Union never more pleasing, and the new President, Herbert Hoover, had recently proudly announced the country near to the total abolition of poverty.

This drop in share prices was purely technical, said one financial wizard that Black Thursday evening: the fundamentals remained unchanged. There was nothing in the business situation to justify any nervousness, scolded another wizard on Friday. On Tuesday, President Hoover agreed with him. Yet another wizard smugly declared to the distraught losers that it was good for business to have the gambling sort of speculator eliminated. On Wednesday, John D. Rockefeller made his famed announcement that 'My son and I have for some days been purchasing sound common stocks,' a remark tantamount to sticking your neck out on the guillotine.

Wall Street went on falling, undeterred by Thanksgiving or Christmas. It fell during 1930, while the Nazis were growing into the biggest political party in Germany. It fell during 1931, while Stalin was violently inaugurating the industrialisation of the USSR. It fell during 1932, while Mussolini was multiplying the Italian fleet to dominate the Mediterranean. The Great Crash became the Great Depression. Black Thursday perpetuated lingering gloom until Friday, 8 July 1932, when the *New York Times*' index hit the middle of the black financial hole, at a quarter of what it had once gloriously been.

It was not this imminent void of depression, perceived through the telescopes of acute financial astronomers, which shattered Wall Street. Nor was it, more prosaically – and more quickly blamed – Britain's return to the gold standard in 1925, nor New York easing credit to help

London. Nor even Winston Churchill happening to be in the Stock Exchange visitors' gallery that dreadful Thursday morning. Its cause was banal: a human frailty, the itch to get something for almost nothing.

Everyday gambling is like religion, the ritualisation of optimism. It is steadfastly condemned, but unnecessarily so, because the odds against anyone becoming a compulsive gambler are infinitely long. We mostly bet for a bit of fun. But the chance of becoming rich without the disadvantage of work had turned, in 1929, from a gamble into a comfortable certainty. This was because, as with investing in the Mississippi or the South Seas, absolutely everybody else was doing it. And everybody else at the same moment surely could not be wrong.

'Anyone taken as an individual is totally sensible and reasonable – as a member of a crowd, he at once becomes a blockhead,' wrote Schiller. Walter Bagehot more kindly decided:

> All people are most credulous when they are most happy; and when much money has just been made, when some people are really making it, when most people think they are making it, there is a happy opportunity for ingenious mendacity.

To which Charles Kindleberger, historian of crashes, adds: 'Attempting to convince speculators of the errors of their ways through talk is generally futile.'

With Euclidean certitude, when mankind progresses speedily along the parallel lines of admonitory reason and joyous lunacy, never will the two meet.

## Lloyd's of London

*Lloyds of London*, a picture made in Hollywood by the great producer Darryl Zanuck in 1936, was 'a historical melodrama of the foundation of the Insurance Company by friends of Nelson in the Napoleonic wars'. It had a script of groaning spars and crashing seas, and claimed 'one of the most daring experiments in film-casting' by starring an unknown, the 23-year-old Tyrone Power. He was six foot, dark-haired, bushy-eyebrowed and well-toothed, 'one of Hollywood's most eligible bachelors', who next starred with ice-skater Sonja Henie in *Lovely to Look At*, and continued as a young romantic until he died at the age of forty-five. Playing opposite him was England's Madeleine Carroll, shortly to flash her suspenders so ravishingly while handcuffed to Robert Donat in *The Thirty-nine Steps*.

The film's theme, Lloyd's, itself voyaged ahead with enviable calm through the perils of peace and war until 1988, when it blew up below decks, facing all hands with overnight bankruptcy.

The Corporation of Lloyd's had originated in London as romantically as in Hollywood, in the prosperity of the Glorious Revolution of 1688. Edward Lloyd was running a coffee house in Lombard Street, north of the ship-choked Thames, where City men meeting over their cups of coffee and chocolate had the notion of offering insurance policies against the perils of the sea. It was insurance by individuals. The backers congealed into small partnerships to underwrite the risk, split the premiums and share any losses. Their liability was unlimited, down to the last farthing in their breeches. The system has not been improved upon today.

These customers of Edward Lloyd attracted the like-minded, the shipping movements were posted on his walls, and when he died in 1713 his name went sailing on across the seven seas. In 1774, the underwriters felt important enough to leave the coffee house for the Royal Exchange, round the corner on Cornhill. They took the name with them, in the English way that sites the venerable Marylebone Cricket Club in St John's Wood, the famed Charing Cross Hospital in Hammersmith, and once had the Oxford Movement in Birmingham.

The prime mover to Cornhill was a Russian *émigré*, John Julius Angerstein. He captained the Lloyd's vessel while it spanked along under the billowing fortunes of the Napoleonic Wars. Lloyd's was now quoting the price of Admiralty: it counselled the Royal Navy where best to route its convoys and even where best to fight its battles, and it kept Lord Nelson and his captains handsomely supplied with gold plate. After Trafalgar, Lloyd's got hold of a log-book written up in calm copperplate amid the gunfire aboard HMS *Euryalus*, which was Nelson's signal-frigate; so Lloyd's could inspire itself for evermore from the only copy of the Admiral's perfect exhortation to Englishmen before the battle. In 1824, Angerstein bought thirty-eight pictures for £57,000 and founded the National Gallery, which never bankrupted anybody.

At Trafalgar, Lloyd's had already a Patriotic Fund for war victims, which became vastly swollen in Britain's wars of the next century. It had published since 1734, *Lloyd's List* of the world's shipping news and, since 1760, *Lloyd's Register of Shipping*, classifying the seaworthiness of every merchant ship afloat. 'A1 at Lloyd's!' was a breezy accolade of straightforward, material honesty, which passed with cheerful sincerity into the language. All of which made Lloyd's later look as safe as one of the Queen's battleships steaming by, dressed overall, in a peacetime naval review in Spithead.

The course for Lloyd's dignification was set by Joseph Marryat MP, father of Frederick (*Mr Midshipman Easy*) Marryat, and accomplished by the Lloyd's Act of 1871. Lloyd's could then legally make its own by-laws, buy and sell what it cared to, and pronounce its own opinions. It stayed roped to marine insurance until 1911, when it was set adrift to insure anything, and with admirable initia-

23

tive covered impartially film stars' legs and in 1935 the life of Adolf Hitler. This policy was taken out by Fritz Thyssen, the German armaments manufacturer and Nazi backer, to whom the Führer manifestly represented a promising investment. Lloyd's rated Hitler at £300.

Lloyd's had its expected losses – one underwriter was paying out £190,000 in 1795. On 9 October 1799, the captured French frigate HMS *Lutine* sailed from Yarmouth to Holland cargoed with £500,000 worth of bullion, and sank with all hands on a sandbank off the Zuider Zee. After Lloyd's had paid up unhesitatingly a £200,000 claim, the salvaged ship's bell was hung in the underwriting room and struck once to signal bad news. Shortly after Lloyd's had moved from its 1928 offices to more stylish ones across Lime Street in the City in 1986, the Lutine Bell started ringing like the telephone.

The descendants of the coffee-house customers were then 25,000 middle-class citizens with at least £100,000 apiece. They had been enjoying some ten years' financial equality under Labour, by paying income tax up to 92 per cent. If they lost money at Lloyd's, unlike losing money at the Stock Exchange, they could get it back from the Government for tax already exacted. Even more conveniently, they did not need to pay the regulation Lloyd's deposit of around £90,000, as their bank happily marketed them a guarantee, perhaps on their house. Men and women pressed into financial partnership with Lloyd's, though it was, like W. S. Gilbert's Ruler of the Queen's Navee, the only ship that they ever had seen.

Lloyd's had always warned solemnly each new underwriting 'name' that they were committed down to their last cufflink, or string of pearls. Now Lloyd's could do it more cheerfully *en masse*. Lloyd's membership rose in three years from 26,000 to 36,000, as people who controlled their family and business finance with enviable prudence crammed to make a profit out of risk, without

24

risk. Lloyd's underwriters, mostly the dimmer products of English public schools, were themselves lulled by their experience of unbroken prosperous years into the agreeable belief that hurricanes hardly ever happened. In a deluge of other people's money, some slipped from underwriting into gambling, writing risks incautiously and seemingly unthinkingly. Brokers presenting one unquestioning underwriter with chancy business – shrewdly, after lunch – called him gleefully 'the nodding donkey'. Like bookmakers, the underwriters reinsured their risks one to another, each taking commission, in an upward spiral that peaked in an immense payout that would never need to be paid.

In the mid-1980s, Lloyd's became the Welfare State of the United States. American workers exposed to asbestos particles were dying of lung cancer and suing their employers, who had been either careless or unscrupulous, the asbestos risk having been plainly recognised in the UK in 1917 and the US in 1947. Though the danger of this asbestosis was increased fivefold in smokers, American courts indignantly awarded the invalids punitive damages, $5 billion between 1980 and 1982 alone. The employers found delightedly that they were covered by forgotten policies written by Lloyd's in the 1930s and 1940s. Then the US woke to a bright environmental dawn, shamed by a century's pollution of nationwide toxic dumping, and found that Lloyd's was conveniently liable for the unimaginable cost of cleaning it up.

Meanwhile, storms, earthquakes, explosions and sinkings assailed Lloyd's like the tempests besetting King Lear. Infuriatingly, Mrs Thatcher had cut the nation's taxes down to size. The peak of the reinsurance spiral crashed ruinously to earth. The loss of cufflinks was not now a laughable possibility, but tomorrow's tragedy. The crew of names mutinied, but were mercilessly flogged by writs. They lost their life savings, their homes, and some, by their own hands, their lives. The newspapers stopped sneering automatically at 'the wealthy people who back Lloyd's', the public perceived that even fat cats can become skeletons, and in a parliamentary debate Labour was startlingly (if ineffectively) supportive.

Lloyd's has now sunk full fathom five, though the captain remains at the helm, bellowing hearty Ahoys! to encourage the officers busy with the rigging. The hapless crew of 'names' suffers the unusual nautical experience of continuing to be violently seasick while deep under-water. The timbers of Lloyd's are shivered, and after three hundred years will shortly float away as more driftwood on the Thames' commercial tides.

THREE

# All that Glisters

On Thursday, 15 July 1897, the steamer *Excelsior* docked in San Francisco packed with excited miners from Alaska, who quickly spread the news that gold was ostentatiously lining the Klondyke river. This stream flowed through an inaccessible corner of Canada, in inhospitable Yukon, up against the Alaskan border. That their startling tale was not another canard was simply proved by the money they started spending. Men who had never before dug into anything more demanding than their dinners had pocketed $100,000 for a few months' work. That Saturday, the *Portland* confirmed the cheerful tidings by sailing into Seattle loaded with one and a half tons of Klondyke gold. The telegraph electrified America.

### Going for Gold

The restless population of the United States had grown accustomed to gold rushes since 1799, when a boy fishing one Sunday in Virginia landed a golden lump big enough to pass the next three years as the family doorstop, before the discovery that it could be turned into $350 cash. The tide of 'forty-niners' had rushed to California, flooding into the Sacramento valley and flowing against its eastern

27

tributaries from the Sierra Nevada, confident there was gold in them thar foothills. The 'fifty-niners', including the Lord Mayor of London's son, were the ones who disappeared into the ravines west of Denver, Colorado, and later turned south to the deceptively goldless cow-grazing pastures of Cripple Creek. In Australia in 1851, the new Colony of Victoria attracted a quarter-million Britons and Chinamen to gold discovered in the environs of Melbourne. In 1886, the rush began in the Witwaters-rand, and did wonders for Cecil Rhodes.

In the 1849 rush, the settlements and farms of California were emptied by the golden voice of easier money upriver. Sailors jumped ship in San Francisco harbour, marooning five hundred vessels. Soldiers deserted, town councils evaporated, merchants vanished with their clerks, lawyers with their criminals, and clerics followed their congregations. Wagon trains hit the trail to California from Kansas City, the two thousand miles taking three months – later, longer, when the horses and mules had eaten up all the route's surrounding grass. Rounding Cape Horn to California from New York under sail took six months; by steamer the voyage was vilely over-crowded and overpriced. Adventurers could anticipate the Panama Canal in crossing the Isthmus by river and mule, hoping then to squeeze on to a packed boat heading north for San Francisco, but meanwhile risking the cholera, malaria and yellow fever that necessitated the inauguration *en route* of three new cemeteries.

The 1897 Klondyke gold rush ran a more civilised course on railroads and shipping lines. The transport companies boosted their golden opportunity with widely advertised enticement, the American and Canadian Pacific ports seeking their own rich pickings along the hopeful path. Blacksmiths, book-keepers, shopkeepers, schoolteachers, fruit-pickers, mechanics, the hopeful workless, the hopeless bankrupts, men who were 'grubstaked' by their fellows clubbing together as though making a bet, all went West and vastly outnumbered the hardened gold-diggers from the gulches of California and Denver. 'Klondicitis' became a national hysteria. Everyone left behind needed an excuse for not going. All American men seemed ready to quit their home comforts, while flocks of actresses, dancers and servant-girls migrated with delicious expectations of lucratively providing them with others.

Once on the Pacific coast, with the enthusiasm of holidaymakers the prospective prospectors kitted themselves out with wide-awake hats, moose-skin boots, moccasins, wigwam slippers, mackinaw blankets, Klondyke stoves, six-shooters (even if the man himself was an honest 'square shooter'), and intriguing but futile items of gold-digging equipment. On arrival by boat at the huts of Juneau up the delightful fiords of south Alaska, the chill of reality set in. Loaded with a year's coffee, bacon and cigarettes, the 'greenhorns' struck north up the Chilkoot Pass, which was six miles long and incorporated a flight of a thousand steps hacked in the ice, creating an unbroken procession of plodding humans savaged by frostbite all the black winter and by mosquitoes in the long days of summer.

Thirty thousand stampeded into misery who had never lived rougher than in a mid-western boarding-house. The 'sourdough' of earlier winters (he retained a fragment of dough from each baking to raise his next loaf) was at ease at 50 below zero. The 'tenderfoot' could barely keep himself fed or dry, and as he knew more about streetcars than horses his beasts sickened and stumbled and died. 'Dead Horse Trail', along the alternative White Pass to the east of Chilkoot, resembled in profusion Balaclava. On 3 April 1898, at Sheep Camp, the last stop before the Chilkoot Pass, seventy-two fortune-hunters were entombed by an avalanche. There was also an epidemic of fatal meningitis.

The arriving 'placer' miner had to 'stake a claim' – and work it without more than three days interruption, lest another could legally 'jump his claim'. He chopped wood to thaw the frozen earth; in the spring he started shovelling mud and gravel from the bed of melting streams. Then he passed his days standing in chilly water while swilling the river sand in a pan, warmed throughout by the expectation of 'pay dirt', to 'strike it rich', to hit a 'bonanza' (how more charmingly expressive a vocabulary have miners bequeathed us than stockbrokers). A labour-saving gold-extracting rocking-machine was contrived later, and further welcome inventiveness conveniently diverted the river first.

It was an unquestionably golden opportunity: there could be $300 in each panful of sand. One miner swilled $25,000 in a day; another, $5,000 in a couple of hours. The amateurs washed fortunes out of the Klondyke before the streams lost their sparkle. They were enjoying a geological joke, a quirk that had erased the conventional indications of deposits which signposted the experienced miners, who went picking at and cracking open the rock crevices to discover the gold-bearing quartz. In the town of Dawson, where the Klondyke river met the Yukon, gold was everywhere that summer of 1898, stacked in used food tins, oil drums and fuel bags. Law and order was maintained by Queen Victoria, by agency of her red-jacketed Mounties.

America in 1898 talked of the Klondyke as thirty years later it talked of Wall Street, when the conversation would turn equally serious. The two places were comparable locations of human frailty. The earlier prospector unthinkingly dared physical disaster, the later speculator heedlessly risked financial ruin, through both trying to become deliciously and unfamiliarly rich. The difference was that the gold miner had to work for it.

### Making Money

Far more comfortable than digging gold from the freezing ground was concocting it indoors. The alchemists who embellish the canvases of Teniers and Holbein the Younger and of Brueghel the Elder sit cosily wrapped in leather and fur while busily puffing their bellows at the coals glowing in brick ovens beneath their hopeful pots. This palmy transmutation of plodding metals into sparkling bullion first struck the inventive Greek god Hermes (the lyre, the alphabet, gymnastics, astronomy and cultivating olives were all his ideas). Alchemists later impressed the seal of Hermes upon their working vessels:

> ... the retort brake,
> And what was sav'd, was put into the pellican,
> And sign'd with Hermes' seal.

Which is – as everybody knows – why our airtight jars of coffee, jam, fish paste and baby food come hermetically sealed.

Because of the eternal Olympian confusion, Hermes sponsored alchemy under another name, the Egyptian god Thoth, who is a dog-headed ape.

Another weakness of the human mind is to be steadfastly misled by the impossible. The Greeks were so fascinated by the shiny, scudding, magical globules of mercury, they sought to free its soul from the cumbersome Aristotelian elements of earth, air, fire and water. You then mated this soul with the soul of sulphur, and got gold. In China, they were doing the same thing by balancing within the basic substance *tao* the opposing

31

elements of *yin* and *yang*, which made life and death, hot and cold, sun and moon, male and female; you had *yin* surging in your bowels and *yang* flowing through your heart.

Alchemy evolved into the science of the Middle Ages. The turning of lead into gold was an intellectual spur as sharp as the urge which achieved atomic energy on 2 December 1942. In the medieval mind, common iron, lead or copper were the mercury of the earth combined with red inflammable sulphur, but contaminated. Dissolve out the impurities, and you had pure gold.

In 1610, they were saying:

> Nature doth first beget th' imperfect; then
> Proceeds she to the perfect . . .
> This night I'll change
> All that is metal in my house to gold.
> And early in the morning will I send
> To all the plumbers and the pewterers,
> And buy their tin and lead up: and to Lothbury,
> For all the copper . . .
> I shall employ it all in pious uses,
> Founding of colleges and grammar schools,
> Marrying young virgins, building hospitals,
> And now and then a church.

To accomplish so rewarding an experiment needed the philosopher's stone. This was an elusive implement to lay hands on. But research for it inspired the incidental discoveries of porcelain, Greek costume jewellery, gunpowder by Roger Bacon, the mercury treatment of syphilis by Swiss physician Paracelsus, and of Dr Glauber's renowned laxative salts.

Like modern scientists, the alchemists were mostly a dull lot. Though St Thomas Aquinas dabbled in it, so did Sir Isaac Newton, and in 1344 Pope John XXII left eighteen million florins widely believed to have been made by it. For a thousand years, they doggedly dug the mines of ignorance, cheered on the surface by millions whose imagination was caught by a cheap way of getting rich.

In 1404, alchemy became a felony in England. Fifty years later Henry VI nationalised it, so that its fabulous products would clink into royal coffers. It occurred to no one that when gold was as plentiful as sawdust it would have the same value. The alchemists meanwhile shrewdly exploited their metallurgical mystique to diversify into necromancers, astrologists, soothsayers and quacks, while fooling their gullible enthusiasts by selling them all that glistered.

With the evolvement of logical chemistry, alchemy evaporated. The last alchemist was 23-year-old, wealthy James Price, né Higginbotham, MA Magdalen, Oxford. On 6 May 1782, he gathered in his laboratory at Guildford, south of London, three lords (including the father of future Prime Minister Lord Palmerston), two baronets, five clerics and numerous doctors and lawyers. One of this impeccable assembly spooned mercury into a Wedgwood mortar, to which Price added a drop of ether and a trace of mysterious white powder. He left it for three-quarters of an hour, strained it, gave it two minutes in a white-hot oven, and turned it into silver. Lord Palmerston then selected a crucible – any crucible – while another member of the audience pounded with a pestle and mortar some borax and charcoal, which everyone had closely inspected. Price added cinnabar, which is red mercuric sulphide, and which was brought to the laboratory beyond suspicion in the hands of a clergyman. He then put in a speck of mysterious red powder, gave it half an hour at white heat . . . and eureka! Gold.

The gold was passed as good gold by the Goldsmiths' Company and by George III. In July, the Regius Professor of Medicine at Oxford bestowed an MD upon Price in the

Sheldonian Theatre at Encaenia. It made a lovely day, with everyone moving across the Broad afterwards for peaches and sherry in the garden at St John's. The following week, Price's experiments were published by Oxford University Press, instantly sold out, and made all the newspapers and magazines. Price was already a member of the Royal Society, which had been founded in 1645 and decorated by Wren, Pepys and Newton, and which was the supreme convocation of British science.

The Royal Society sucked its teeth.

None of the eminent audience at Guildford had been a scientist. The Royal Society wanted the formula of the mysterious powders. Price said he had none left. It would make him ill to create any more. Anyway, they were too expensive. The whole experiment was too expensive. It cost seventeen pounds to make four pounds' worth of gold. Ridiculous. Oh, that denial which he had published, of the mercury borne by the cleric already containing gold, well, it was not, er, entirely correct. The red powder was anyway only arsenic. There was really no point in the Royal Society badgering him to repeat the experiment. He was beginning to understand how Galileo felt. In Oxford, they were pulling the Regius Professor of Medicine's leg.

The following summer, Price excitedly invited all the Fellows of the Royal Society from its headquarters at Burlington House down to Guildford. He was to repeat his experiments on 31 July 1783. Only three Fellows troubled to reach the laboratory, where Price had all his apparatus in glowing readiness, swallowed a glass of cyanide, and dropped dead.

> Rather than be bray'd, sir, I'll believe
> That alchemy is a pretty kind of game,
> Somewhat like tricks o' the cards, to cheat a man
> With charming.

O rare Ben Jonson. The priceless product of alchemy was *The Alchemist*.


### Bubbling On

The 250 years after the South Sea catastrophe rang regularly with its echoes. They emitted forty financial crashes. These affected all the civilised countries, and were precipitated by irresponsible speculation in such varied items as canals, railways, sugar, cotton, wheat, coffee, gold, homesteads, airliners and each other's currencies.

Like the fevers of childhood, each attack of speculation brought immunity against another one. And like those infections, the immunity faded. As this immune period among speculators spanned only sharp human memory for an unpleasant occasion of foolishness, the protection so imparted was understandably short.

Has the Bubble burst?

'Whatever the reason, it seems clear that there is no comparison between the present worldwide bull market and the great speculative bubbles of the past ... the finances of major corporations are soundly based. The public is not carried away with speculative fever,' wrote the *Financial Times* reassuringly, 573 days before the Friday in 1987 when Wall Street fell 108 points, to be followed on the Tuesday by another 508, and when the unforetold winds which that weekend had flattened Britain also blew away from the London Stock Exchange £93 billion.

The 'sapient nincompoops' blamed for a London bank crash of May 1886 are a hardy breed. And today's instantaneous communications give modern crashes an atomic *éclat*.

The edge between sharp business and sharp practice is

blunt. Through these 250 years since the South Sea Bubble pass shiftily men like Horatio Bottomley, MP for Hackney, owner of the fearless and fiercely patriotic weekly *John Bull*. After the Great War, Bottomley patriotically also invested for John Bull, but emptied his pockets instead. His 'Victory Bond Club' swiftly drew half a million pounds for a lottery to win the interest accruing on these impeccable government securities. As the winners' names appeared only in *John Bull*, Bottomley could acquire some valuable *noms de plume*.

Suspicious losers were shortly demanding their money back, and in 1922 Bottomley was flamboyantly conducting his own defence at the Old Bailey: 'The jury is not yet born who would convict me on these charges. It is unthinkable.' He shook his finger at the sword of justice behind the judge's head: 'That sword would drop from its scabbard if you gave a verdict of guilty against me.' The jury took less than half an hour to find out. He faced seven years making mail-bags (*Prison Visitor*: 'Ah, Bottomley, sewing?' *Prisoner*: 'No, reaping.').

Clarence Hatry by 1929 had built upon his original business of penny-in-the-slot machines a financial empire upon which, like the British one, it was clear to the world that the sun would never set, until he was imprisoned at the Old Bailey for forgery and impoverished his devotees. The widely revered Swedish Match King, Ivar Kreuger, shot himself in Paris in 1932 to avoid the awkwardness following massive embezzlement and forgery. Serge Stavisky shot himself clad in a ski-suit in Chamonix in 1934 (or the police did), causing riots in Paris and tumbling the French Government. Robert Maxwell sank in 1991, to the consternation of all the people who had floated him.

Which proves that human beings should not be trusted with money, particularly other people's.

FOUR

# Ghoulies and Ghosties

The man on the Clapham omnibus – a passenger conceived by the English appeal judge Lord Bowen, towards the end of the nineteenth century – motors on through history with frighteningly odd notions about the sensible, everyday world which he famously personifies. He becomes restless with the rational explanations of its mechanics, offered to him cordially by the busy people who know how they work. He prefers the mysterious, fantastic and frightening ones. Which is understandable, Clapham being such a dull place to go to.

The man and woman on the Clapham bus are thus easy prey for quacks, charlatans, tricksters and the exploiters of material or immaterial stimulants to an excitable imagination. Such intoxication is usually amusing and harmless. Sometimes it turns wicked and murderous.

### The Witches of Salem

In January 1692, Betty Parris, the nine-year-old daughter of the minister at the Calvinist chapel in Salem Village north of Boston, her eleven-year-old cousin Abigail, and Ann Putnam, the twelve-year-old daughter of the parish clerk, started a joke which ended in the ceremonious killing of twenty neighbours, the jailing of a four-year-old girl, and the judicial execution of a dog.

The three children were crawling under chairs and into holes in the garden, striking odd postures and making wild gestures, uttering loud cries and gabbling meaningless sentences. The grotesquerie grew more violent, until the distraught parents sent for Dr Griggs, who diagnosed their little ones as bewitched.

Prayers were applied, neighbouring ministers summoned, but the girls performed the more exuberantly, screaming at the Lord's Prayer and throwing the Bible about. Everyone was horror-struck at confronting the fearsome work of the Devil within the muddy streets and clapboard houses of Salem. Through which witch did the Devil work? The adults nervously ran familiar faces through their minds. The three girls were pressed to tell. They had no idea. The adults suggested a few names. The girls agreed in a single shout: it was Tituba.

The Rev Samuel Parris had been a merchant in Barbados, where he exchanged commerce for the Gospel two years earlier and accepted the living at Salem Village, after haggling over the £66 stipend. He brought with him a West Indian slave woman Tituba, who everyone now remembered had amused the children with tricks and tales of Caribbean voodoo. The three young patients were encouraged further. They cried out the name of Sarah Good, a local beggar and pipe-smoker, who was abandoned by her husband and pregnant; and of Sarah Osburn, who was old and bedridden. The children then developed blockage in the throat, caused by the Devil stuffing balls down them. Also, they felt the prickling of thorns all over. On leap year day 1692, the three women were arrested.

Salem Village was founded in 1672. It became Danvers in 1757, which George II disallowed; thus it could proudly incorporate 'The King Unwilling' in the new town seal. The early New Englanders lived amid threatening unexplored forests, their settlements scattered, the roads lonely, the climate inclined to be disagreeable, the life hard and the religion gloomy. Their nature was superstitious and mystical, and the inhabitants of Salem had a widespread reputation for being quarrelsome.

Everybody believed in witchcraft as in lightning – it was dangerous and deadly, but with luck remotely unlikely to hit oneself. Its existence was beyond question. The Bible spoke of the whoredoms and witchcrafts of Jezebel, of Nineveh as the mistress of witchcrafts, and God had commanded plainly in Exodus: 'Thou shalt not suffer a witch to live.' There had already been supernatural trouble in the Massachusetts Bay Colony, when in 1688 the four children of Boston stonemason John Godwin had fits, for which the Irish washerwoman Witch Glover was hanged, though the treatment failed.

The day after their arrest, the three Salem witches were interrogated by two magistrates, who arrived with pomp before a crowd cramming the wooden meeting-house. Their questions were straightforward, being based on their conviction of the prisoners' guilt.

> 'Sarah Good, what evil spirit have you familiarity with?'
> 'None.'
> 'Have you made no contracts with the Devil?'
> 'No.'
> 'Why do you hurt these children?'
> 'I do not hurt them. I scorn it.'
> 'How came they thus tormented?'
> 'What do I know?'
> 'Sarah Good, do you not see now what you have done? Why do you not tell us the truth? Why do you thus torment these poor children?'
> 'I do not torment them.'

On 7 March, Sarah Good was taken to Boston jail, where she had her baby, which died. So was Sarah

Osburn, where she was heavily chained up until 10 May, when she died.

The minister's slave Tituba had meanwhile tried to shift the blame.

'Sarah Good and Osburn would have me hurt the children, but I would not.'

'When did you see them?'

'Last night at Boston.'

'How did you go?'

'We ride upon sticks and are there presently.'

'Do you go through the trees or over them?'

'We see nothing, but are there presently.'

'What is this appearance you see?'

'Sometimes it is like hog, and sometimes like a great dog. I have seen two cats, a red cat and a black cat.'

'What attendants hath Sarah Good?'

'A yellow-bird, it did suck her between her fingers.'

'What hath Sarah Osburn?'

'Yesterday, she had a thing like a woman, with two legs and wings. Another thing, hairy, it goes upright like a man, it hath only two legs.'

But she went to Boston jail, too.

Suddenly, everyone in Salem was seeing witches. Women were swooning in the street; children were having fits everywhere. Two hundred supernatural suspects were arrested. If they did not destroy their neighbours' souls and bodies themselves, everyone knew they deputed their evil powers to cats and dogs and spiders, or stuck pins into puppets. At the beginning of June, a witches' court was established, with five judges sent up from Boston.

Each prisoner entered the meeting-house to face her accusers, a gang of little girls who immediately screamed and fell on the floor. A deadly pantomime was played. If the prisoner clasped her hands they cried she was pinching them; if she bit her lip they shouted she was biting

**40**

them; if she tottered they screamed she was crushing them; if she took a step she tormented their feet. When the girls complained that pins had been malevolently pricked into their flesh, they produced the pins (they still have them in Salem, in a bottle, rusted, their heads formed of twisted wire). Such practical evidence was overwhelming.

Hysteria ran through Salem as fearsomely as the previous year's smallpox epidemic, but nobody noticed it. The children's behaviour was less suspect of deceit than were their everyday tantrums over refusing food. And anyone murmuring doubtful criticism of their virtuousness was in trouble, like Martha Corey.

> 'Well, tell us what you know of this matter.'
> 'Why, I am a gospel woman, and do you think I can have to do with witchcraft too?'
> The children: 'There is a man whispering in her ear.'
> 'What did he say to you?'
> 'We must not believe all that these distracted children say.'
> 'Cannot you tell what that man whispered?'
> 'I saw nobody.'
> 'But did you hear?'
> 'No.'
> 'Here was extreme agony of the afflicted,' the Rev Samuel Parris noted sympathetically about the children.

Martha Corey was hanged on 22 September. Her husband Giles was a hostile witness, but his testimony not being thought enthusiastic enough he was arrested on 19 April. Stricken in jail with matrimonial remorse, Giles Corey bequeathed his property to his two sons-in-law; then, to ensure against his will's invalidation by his conviction and inevitable execution, he stood mute in court when invited to plead. This meant, through legal

41

procedure, that three days before his wife's execution he was laid naked in a field and pressed to death with rocks.

They asked young Sarah Carter:

'How long hast thou been a witch?'
'Ever since I was six years old.'
'How old are you now?'
'Near eight years old.'
'Who made you a witch?'
'My mother.'

Mother Martha was hanged.

Testimony grew daily more lurid, as spectres, dreams, visions and fancies readily solidified into evidence. The Devil and his witches became commonplace in Salem, toasting each other in their victims' blood. Even a 'not guilty' verdict failed for Rebecca Nurse: the outraged mob frightened the judges into reversing it, and the church excommunicated her for good measure. George Burroughs was hanged because little Ann Putnam had met his two former wives in their winding-sheets, red-faced with anger at his having murdered them. Ann's young uncle Joseph proclaimed Salem's zealous crusade a pious fraud, but needed to keep himself fully armed and his horse ready saddled day and night. The smart citizens of nearby Andover seized on the idea that the safest way to prevent the accusation of being a witch was to become the accuser of somebody else.

The cauldron at Salem bubbled the brisker with the arrival of the Rev Cotton Mather from Boston, where he had been stirring the same brew. He had written *Memorable Providences Relating to Witchcraft and Possession*, and was fervid to be God's sword-arm. Most men hope to become angels, they were saying in Massachusetts, but nothing would have contented the Rev Cotton Mather than to be an archangel.

The condemned were carted to Gallows Hill, a mile

out of town, where the Rev Cotton Mather enthusiastically supervised their executions. They were hanged by the High Sheriff, by being deprived of a ladder while noosed to the branches of an oak tree, then buried shallowly in the Gallows Hill crevices. It was all in order, because on 8 June the higher General Court had revived an old law that held witchcraft to be a capital offence.

One female witch was hanged on 10 June 1692, five on 19 July, four men and a woman on 19 August, seven women and a man on 22 September. Over these ultimate swaying bodies the Rev Nicholas Noyes, pastor of the First Church at Salem Town, lamented: 'What a sad sight it is to see eight firebrands of hell hanging there,' an expression of malevolent smugness so amazing to be excusable only by the totality of its internal blindness and external ignorance. Four-year-old Dorcas Good, her mother executed, was released from her imprisonment for biting people on the Devil's behalf. The dog died unnoticed.

People were beginning to get worried in Massachusetts. Sir William Phipps had arrived in the colony as Governor only on 14 May, but knew his King's remote subjects. Sir William was born by the Kennebeck river in Maine, started work as a ship's carpenter, became a Boston captain, made a fortune raising a Spanish treasure-ship off the Bahamas, and had been provost-marshal of New England five years earlier (two years after Salem, he was summoned home for 'undignified conduct' in doing nothing against the Indians and the French, neither of whom were troubled with witches).

In October, Sir William halted the Court of Oyer and Terminer trying witchcraft. In May, he pardoned everyone. The witches who crammed the prisons of Salem, Boston, Cambridge and Ipswich were released after paying their board and jailers' fees. Tituba was freed into the lifelong servitude of a colonist who settled up her accumulated debt of a half-crown a week.

The lethal whirlwind dropped. The judges were publicly penitent and the jurors excused themselves through their ignorance. The smart citizens of Andover brought suits for slander against their accusers. Cotton Mather went back to Boston and wrote *More Wonders of the Invisible World*. Who came best out of Salem was Arthur Miller, in 1953, with *The Crucible*.


### Convicta et Combusta

The witches of Salem are a bright, sharp microscopical image of the psychological germs which infected the mind of Europe for two and a half centuries. The victims of this terrible plague were tens of thousands of inoffensive and unremarkable women and men, old, poor, sick, unwanted, often odd, sometimes mad. In some German cities they were at one time being burnt at the rate of 600 a year: 'Two every day, if we leave out the Sundays, when it is to be supposed that even this madness refrained from its work,' Charles Mackay contemplates in *Extraordinary Popular Delusions*.

A witch was defined by Queen Elizabeth I's attorney-general Lord Coke as 'a person who hath conference with the Devil to consult with him or to do some act'. The Devil himself was the name given by Christians to the god of people who simply preferred to persist in being pagan.

The Devil, too, moved in mysterious ways. He appeared as a stag, goat, bull, dog or cat, or as the inconspicuous man in black. The witches, who gathered in covens of thirteen, were his priests, and they had been dancing in the churchyards since the early fourteenth century. The witches' Sabbaths were the Devil's own

44

cheerful conventions, held in the countryside at Candlemas in February, on Walpurgis Night on the eve of May Day, at Lammas in August, and the big one on All Hallow E'en. The revels started at nightfall and ended at cockcrow, with fertility rites for humans, for herds, and for the crops, and some sexual performances in public. It was much more fun than going to church.

David Teniers' picture *Departure for the Sabbat* shows a naked blonde eagerly astride her broomstick, awaiting launching by a witch amid the hellhag's skulls and potions and her batlike and froglike demons. Jan Ziarnko, a Polish artist who flourished in Paris at the turn of the sixteenth century, presents more realistically a joyous fairground of stark-naked men, women, children and babes, worshipping the enthroned Grand Master who is wearing his stag's head and antlers, all feasting, singing, and dancing to the five-piece band. The riders on broomsticks and on airborne goats, the flying cats and dragons, are not part of the picnic but fantasies in the magic vapour of a cauldron of toads and snakes boiling on a fire of blazing skulls. But it was the fantasy which took human imagination.

Theologically, a witch was someone playing for the other side. As Christianity became stronger and more popular it began to win the matches. The new religion enjoyed the comradeship of the law in overcoming the ancient one. Heathens were condemnable, but witches were shudderingly vile because everyday calamities – climatic, economic, physical, or swiftly fatal – were inflicted by the Devil, who the Christians saw as hairy, horned, long-tailed, cloven-hoofed and dragon-winged, and working his malevolence through his hags. Then there was the incubus and succubus tendency, quite disgusting. Heretics were plain to see, but the witches needed hunting out.

Witchcraft put paid to the powerful Knights Templars.

45

Philip IV of France wanted rid of them for their money, so he noised it abroad that the Templars had sold their souls to the Devil, that they roasted babies on slow fires, applied the trickling fat to the beard of the Devil's image, drank the powdered bodies of dead knights, and indulged in unspeakable debauchery, which included novices having to kiss the superior's arse.

The Templars were arrested *en masse*, with help from the Inquisition, on 14 September 1307. Imprisoned, and tortured into confession on the rack, they were then burnt, fifty-nine of them together, in a field ouside Paris by a slow fire. In 1431, Joan of Arc was targeted with convenient imputations of witchcraft by the English. She suffered schizophrenic symptoms, the hearing of voices: and thus she led also a sad army of the deranged, who were shortly to be burnt solely for their mental peculiarities.

In 1488, Pope Innocent VIII uttered a Bull itemising the horrors of witchcraft, from copulation with fiends to ruining the *vendange*, and he armed the inquisitors with apostolic powers of punishment. However wild the accusation of witchcraft, the rack reliably brought agonised confession. Or, less painfully, victims were stripped naked and pinpricked all over to discover the numb spot, the stamp of the Devil's own; or driven to confess in despair, in the hope of saving their lives. The lunatic trial ended inevitably with the grimly satisfied entry in the criminal register, *convicta et combusta*. The lucky ones were first strangled at the stake by the hangman. The less fortunate were burnt 'alive and quick'. If you were rich enough, though, you could be fined instead. Simply to doubt the reality of witchcraft was heresy, and equally fatal.

Witchcraft shared the blame for the Reformation, but the Lutherans and the Calvinists were as hot on witches as the Catholics. It became a dreadful crime in England in 1562 under Elizabeth I, who, with the change of ends in the religious game, was persecuting the Catholics with the fervour that her sister Mary had applied to the Protestants, while expressing her admirable independence of mind by referring to excommunications as 'the Pope's crackfarts'.

When James I was still James VI of Scotland, he published in Edinburgh in 1587 his treatise *Demonologie*, stating forthrightly: 'Witches ought to be put to death, according to the law of God, the civil and imperial law, and the municipal law of all Christian nations.' The crime was so abominable that the flimsiest evidence would do: word of young children or of crooks, or mispronunciation of the Lord's Prayer. James himself favoured a less fussy way of obtaining proof. The accused were wrapped naked in a blanket, thumbs tied to big toes, and thrown into the river – innocent, they sank and drowned; guilty, they floated and were burnt.

The evidence of Sir Thomas Browne – the most scholarly of doctors, author of *Religio Medici* – in 1664 condemned Amy Duny and Rose Cullender of St Edmondsbury in Suffolk for bewitching children into fits, and causing them to vomit nails, and to see ghostly ducks and mice. The little victims improved within half an hour of the witches' conviction, and were gratifyingly fit when their tormentors were hanged. The King of Sweden became concerned during the summer of 1669 about witches in the village of Mohra, so he sent a commission which burnt twenty-three in one fire, to joyous applause from thousands of spectators. The next day, they burnt fifteen children, had the residual thirty-two witches executed in the next village, and sentenced fifty-six more lucky children to a public whipping weekly for a year.

Some witches unashamedly ran a sound business in love-potions – which enjoyed a good sale to ageing gallants chasing reluctant virgins – fertility drugs, veterinary cures, pestilence prophylactics, wax images of sexual or commercial rivals to be pierced with pins, and straightforward poisons. Your visit to the remote cottage or grotto was secret, also desperate: if a witch could give no hope in your troubles, then you were beyond any. In 1612, in the Lancashire Forest of Pendle, the near eighty-year-olds Elizabeth Southerns and Ann Whittle, whose professional names were Old Demdike and Old Chattox, were commercially doing splendidly, if in competition, until arrested with their families and condemned on the evidence of Old Demdike's granddaughter (though Old Demdike died before she could be hanged).

Under Charles I in 1634, a pack of witches was flushed from the same forest and accused on the evidence of Ned Robinson, the young son of a local mason, whose blackmailing threats of accusations had brought him the price of a cow or two. Seventeen women were found guilty, but the judge shied from the death sentences. Four of the younger were taken from Lancaster jail to the Ship Tavern at Greenwich, to be stripped and searched for witches' marks by midwives selected by Dr Harvey, who also discovered the circulation of the blood. Charles I was so concerned with the case that he himself was present.

Nothing was found except old medicinal leech-marks, though these were suspicious as the suckling-marks of a witch's familiar. Young Ned then confessed to the dubious Secretary of State Sir Francis Windebank that the charges 'merely proceeded out of mine own brain'. It was all to divert a beating from his father for forgetting to fetch in the cows. Harrison Ainsworth later wrote the novel *The Lancashire Witches* which, swiftly adapted for the stage, opened at the Adelphi Theatre on 3 January 1848 with a chorus of nuns rising from the grave to dance with amorous ghosts.

The more witches they burned the more they found to burn, through the proud zeal and ferocious self-righteousness of the witch-hunters. James Sprenger in Germany, author of the standard handbook on witch-hunting, the 1494 *Malleus Maleficarum* (*Hammer of Evil*), lit the fuse for five hundred women a year. In England during the Civil War, smart, sweeping moustached, spurred and cloaked Matthew Hopkins from Manningtree in Essex, the self-titled 'Witch-finder General', became a national hero with a score of sixty a year. He charged 20 shillings a head, plus travelling and living expenses, also for his two assistants. But he lost his fans, who turned upon him in a Suffolk village, stripped him, tied his thumbs and toes, blanketed him, and threw him in the duck-pond. There is no record whether he sank or floated, which was immaterial to his end in 1647, hanged as a sorcerer. While the Long Parliament sat, 3,000 witches were killed.

In 1716, a Huntington woman and her nine-year-old daughter were hanged for raising a thunderstorm by removing their stockings, but people were growing more sophisticated. The Act of James I in 1604 that confirmed witchcraft as a capital offence was repealed in 1736. Witches were downgraded to suffering the penalty of fortune-tellers and conjurers, the pillory. People were still seeing witches in Hastings in 1830, and on Walpurgis Night in Bavaria they were prudently ringing the church bells, lighting bonfires, clashing pots and pans, letting loose the dogs and screaming, 'Witch flee!' into the 1920s. But perhaps it was just a joke, like the witchcraft which persists today as an excuse for sexual antics.

### Why Witches?

To the man on the Canterbury hay-cart, whatever he could not understand, whatever frightened him – storms, fires, droughts, deformity, madness, sickness, death – was caused by the omnipotent and unfathomable supernatural. The existence of such powers, which could favour a man as well as blight him, was forthrightly proved by glancing at any joyous or suffering human possessed by them. A witch was an agent of this awesome force, as plain as a pikeman was of the King's.

The ensuing witch mania illustrates a murderous human frailty. Witches were slaughtered through mankind's sad tendency to turn savagely upon a section of itself – if reliably defenceless – out of fear, spite or ignorance, for selfish advantage, or for simple enjoyment. Examples have made too many blots on the pages of history to necessitate itemisation. They have been spattered impartially by the high motives of religion or by the low convenience of politics.

Another human psychological frailty was instanced by the repeated evidence of children against witches, so convenient, so convincing, so touching, and so horrifying. Hysteria – the theatricalisation of life – is common in children. It expresses itself readily in twitching and trembling, fits, apparent blindness, vomiting, paralysis, posturing, screaming, the 'globus hystericus' of impeded swallowing. All of which lack physical cause, swiftly vanish, attract attention, achieve advantage or escape disfavour, and are liable to spread among other children instantaneously like laughter at the pantomime.

There was one physical cause of this bloody lunacy. In Aldous Huxley's account *The Devils of Loudun*, the devils orgasmically possessed seventeen young Ursuline nuns in 1634, causing the handsome *curé* Urbain Grandier to be tortured by having his legs crushed, his body shaved all over, then burnt, and his ashes shovelled to the four winds. The nuns, who had defied the most expert exorcists, were perhaps coiffed cases of hysteria. Or they were cases of ergot poisoning. *Claviceps purpurea*, the fungus which makes purple spurs on the ears of 'smutty' rye in a wet summer, contains a chemical like

LSD which incites similar hallucinations. Many witches executed in Europe and New England may have suffered fatally from the remote effects of their neighbours' eating bad rye bread.

The powers of darkness vanished as the spreading light of science revealed rational explanations of Nature's perils and malevolence. Science has now been discovered, by the scientifically ignorant but otherwise enviably intelligent, as the new witchcraft. The nonsense began in *The Times* of 13 April 1992, which became anxious about 'the monster of science' and quoted nervously from a popular book complaining about 'the appalling spiritual damage that science has done and how much more it can still do', adding that: 'It is spiritually corrosive, burning away ancient authorities and traditions. It cannot really co-exist with anything.'

Science is modest. Like religion, it is man-made: it is man's study of natural forces. It applies a tape-measure to these phenomena, tries to understand them, and to manipulate them for human good. Scientists are scornfully complimented on 'taking on the mantle of wizards, sorcerers and witch-doctors'. But it is only humans suffering from the widespread frailty of superstition who invest science with power which it does not have. nuclear bomb?

Science emphasises humblingly the miserable capacity of the human mind, which is limited by its inelasticity to the understanding, in principle, only of railway timetables.

'The forms or conditions of Time and Space, as Kant will tell you, are nothing in themselves – only our way of looking at things,' the Autocrat of the Breakfast-Table, Oliver Wendell Holmes – himself a scientist, Professor of Anatomy at Harvard for thirty-five years – was gently reminding the schoolmistress one morning in 1858. Our universe may be but an atom spinning in the breakfast boiled egg of some amiable inhabitant of another one.

There seems no point in becoming overexcited about this.

The 'inner desolation' of human beings that is fashionably blamed on science is an ungrateful interpretation of science's releasing humanity from the anguish of a spouse, or a child, dead from some everyday infection. This was an everyday disaster before the discovery of antibiotics. The prissy complaint that 'scientism' dehumanises natural child-rearing ignores that without science's reduction of infant mortality the grousers might have no child to rear.

It is all tilting at windmills (which are valuable expressions of applied science). *The Times* slightingly cited Pandit Nehru of India: 'It is science *alone* that can solve the problems of hunger and poverty, of insanitation and illiteracy, or superstition and deadening custom and tradition, of vast resources running to waste, of a rich country inhabited by starving people.'

Nehru was as right as Galileo.

Pharmacology and plumbing have done more for us frail humans than philosophy. Spiritual dignity, like earthy Anita Loos' kissing your hand, 'may make you feel very very good', but the effect of sound drains and effective medicaments, like her 'diamond and safire bracelet', lasts for ever.

# FIVE

# Long-leggety Beasties

In 1874, 31-year-old Abraham Stoker, a Dublin Civil Servant, published *The Duties of Clerks of Petty Sessions in Ireland*. Nineteen years later, as Bram Stoker, he wrote *Dracula*, which sold a million copies. It created the image of the vampire, elegant in white tie and tails, flitting through the moonlight to sink his elongated canines into the sleeping jugulars of Transylvania's most beautiful women.

## In Cold Blood

Count Dracula was modelled on a prince, Vlad Domn, a descendant of Ghenghis Khan who ruled fifteenth-century Walachia, and who never really induced anaemia in anyone. The vampire craze began when Walachia and Bucharest were occupied by the Austrians after the treaty of Passarowitz, which ended their war with Turkey in 1718. The Austrians were puzzled to discover a local propensity for killing the already dead.

Bodies were exhumed in the benevolent and sanctifying presence of the priest, then had a sharpened stake driven through the heart with a mallet. This was necessitated by any outbreak of swift and inexplicable deaths in

**53**

the neighbourhood. It was common knowledge that a recent corpse had flitted by night to the deathbeds, lay heavily upon the sufferers, sucked their blood, and by strangulation caused the agonised cries of suffocation as they breathed their last. At dawn, the vampire returned to his coffin and closed the lid. To rid the village of this nuisance you drove a stake through his heart, whereupon he changed in time into an innocuous skeleton. Vlad Domn, also known as Vlad Tepes – *teapa* is Romanian for stake – was an enthusiast for the practice of impaling criminals. In 1462, he had 20,000 of them dangling in his citadel at once, a sight that caused instant retreat of the invading Turks. He was also an enthusiastic bat-keeper.

The post-mortem signs of a typical vampire, after the corpse had been two or three months underground, were striking. The body gave off no stink, nor was it decomposed; the hair had grown, the nails had been shed by the new ones budding underneath, another skin was forming under the peeling old one, and there was fresh blood on the mouth, sucked from last night's victims. The limbs were supple, and he had an erection, with which he was inclined, between bloodsucking, to bother the widows.

After staking by the villagers, more alien blood would spurt from the vampire's ears, eyes, nose and mouth. The head was then cut off with the sexton's spade, his heart was boiled in wine, and, as an extra precaution, his body burnt. To stop a cholera epidemic, you needed to direct the stake through the mouth. Less troublesomely, you could hammer into the grave a sharp stake, on which the vampire would carelessly impale itself when leaving at midnight. Or you might ceremoniously fire into, not over, the grave, though a flying vampire could be bagged only with a silver bullet. The best day to stake a vampire's grave was Saturday, because vampires did not travel on Saturdays.

The rotting of any corpse by chemical and bacterial activity is a stereotyped process described in all pathology books. It brings bloating, discoloration of the blood, leaking from the body cavities, distension of the skin, blisters, and a bloody froth to the lips, from the gas of putrefaction in the abdomen that compresses the lungs. To the scientifically ignorant, these processes in a flesh-clad body were understandably imagined to be a continuation of those of life. The vampires were luckier scapegoats than the witches for epidemics, sickness and death: they evaded vengeful torture and execution by being already dead.

The Romanians worried that by flying over a kinsman's corpse a bat could be transformed into a vampire, but the vampire bat is an animal of fiction, not of folklore. Nobody had seen a bloodthirsty vampire, nor one anywhere outside his violated grave. Everybody had seen a werewolf, because there were plenty of hungry wolves violating graves in the darkness to eat the corpses. If the wolves devoured instead living sheep and sheepdogs, then the shepherds could revenge themselves by accusing their neighbours of turning into werewolves at nightfall and ravaging the flocks. This commercial crime carried the utmost punishment of burning 'alive and quick'. The Church readily ratified the transformation: if King Nebuchadnezzar, in the Book of Daniel, 'was driven from men, and did eat grass as oxen, and his body was wet with the dew of heaven', why should not commoners turn into wolves?


## Mixed Monsters

To see animals which are unlike any others is a privilege that has been enjoyed by favoured humans since the fauns and satyrs gambolled away into mythology. Their inheritor was Bigfoot.

In 1958, a lumberjack driving a bulldozer in the forests of Washington State noticed bare human footprints in the mud, sixteen inches long and seven inches wide. A wild, hair-covered man had already been found in British Columbia, in a railway tunnel in 1884. Another in Manitoba had been reported in *The Times* in 1784. Bigfoot seemed one of the family.

Plaster casts of his feet were collected by his devotees, and he appeared in 1967 as a fat, big-bottomed hairy creature on a sensational snatch of film taken by a journalist, who the previous year had published a popular book about him. Nobody since has photographed Bigfoot, though so many people have looked for him that the Bigfoot Information Center was founded in Oregon. It publishes the *Bigfoot News*, and is satisfied that 96 wayfarers have observed him. In Oregon, Bigfoot is a protected species. You risk five years in the county jail for shooting him, whether he exists or not.

Across the world, on the Menlung Glacier in the Himalayas, in November 1951 explorer Eric Shipton photographed in the snow footprints the same size as Bigfoot's. They were imprinted by the Yeti, which emits a high-pitched noise heard by Lord Hunt, who led the Everest Expedition in 1953. The *Daily Mail* in 1954 mounted a magnificent expedition – it necessitated 300 Sherpas to carry the bags – from London to Nepal, which was by then issuing expensive Yeti-hunting licences. The *Daily Mail* did not see the Yeti, and neither has anybody else from Europe, though two mountaineers one night in 1970 thought they did.

Yeti footprints had anyway been reported thirty years earlier, by the Everest expedition of 1921, to *The Times*, who first printed its Tibetan name, the 'Abominable Snowman'. The locals had been seeing the Yeti for years before that – it was to them a mixture of man, animal and religious symbolism – and *The Times* reported also that one evening in 1911 an officer mentioning in the Gurkha mess his meeting the Yeti that morning found 'they took it rather as a matter of course'. The first Yeti footprints were displayed earlier still, to a British major by his Sherpas in 1889, but he explained patiently that they were the tracks of a snow bear, *Ursus isabellinus*.

The *Daily Mail* that Yeti season was a richly experienced monster-hunting journal. In the spring of 1933, the couple who ran the Drumnadrochit Hotel overlooking Loch Ness saw a whale-like creature churning in the water. The *Daily Mail* was hot on the scent. It dispatched a big-game hunter from Africa, who the following September sensationally discovered, and made plaster casts of, the Monster's footprints on the steep Loch shore, though the imprints were shortly found to be of some joker's hippo-foot umbrella stand. Nobody had noticed that the poor thing walked on only one leg. Six months later, the *Daily Mail* made amends by publishing the floating Monster's photograph, which was sent them by a passing consultant gynaecologist, and taken on 1 April.

The United Kingdom went Monster mad. They floodlit nearby Inverness. Scotland's hotels were crammed with visitors, even in the season of Hogmanay and Burns Night, when Englishmen are baffled that the place is climatically habitable. The long, narrow, deep, misty Loch was highly suggestive of monsters, particularly with the encouragement from local lore of black, man-eating water horses, the kelpies. The Monster was seen 120 times before World War Two, and benefited afterwards from wartime scientific advances when it was pursued underwater by cameras and sonar.

On such technical evidence, the Monster was painted by Sir Peter Scott, the son of Scott of the Antarctic. His swimming Monster was huge, humped and flippered, and classified by Sir Peter as *Nessiteras rhombopteryx* (which is the anagram of 'Monster hoax by Sir Peter S'). The Natural History Museum in London turned its nose up. It was doubtful about a tropical, ocean-going, fish-eating plesiosaurus – which had been extinct for seventy million years – making its home not far from Balmoral.

The Museum asked awkward questions. How does it breathe without poking out a snout? How does it feed on the Loch's meagre food stocks? How does it do poo-poos, when none have been found? How does it reproduce, when no eggs have surfaced? How does it die, when no bodies have floated up? The Museum suspected that the underwater photographs were blown-up shots of plastic bags, weeds, trees, or disintegrating picnics. A 24-hours-a-day sonar scan in the summer of 1982 found, one May afternoon, something moving at the bottom of Loch Ness, 700 feet below, that was more powerful than a shoal of fish. The next year, another sonar spoilt the story by discovering that underwater landslides were common in the steep, stream-pierced depths of Scottish lochs.

An undaunted Loch Ness Investigation Bureau had earlier posted volunteers scanning the bleak water from daybreak to dusk. Three thousand enthusiastic seekers had told the Bureau that they had seen the Monster, all leaving their name and address. The Monster got on television, and far more people were instantly viewing it in the fascinating flesh. Books are still being profitably written about it, and the tourist office at Inverness is everlastingly crammed with people seeking final directions to it from starting points all over the world.

While Scotsmen peered for strange creatures in the peaty depths of a loch, Americans sought them among the stars.

## Pie in the Sky

On 24 June 1947, Kenneth Arnold, a businessman from Idaho, was piloting his plane over the Bigfoot country of Mount Rainier, Washington, when he saw 'a chain of small saucer-like things at least five miles long swerving in and out of the mountain peaks'. It may have been swirling snow or small clouds, but the next morning 'flying saucers' were in all the newspapers.

Soon, everyone was seeing them all over America, then all over the world. On 22 January 1948, the alarmed US Air Force put into operation Project Saucer. The Swedes then mentioned that they had been seeing saucers regularly since early 1946 – they were fired across their country by the Russians – but they may have been wild geese.

Mr Arnold was far from the first heavenly spotter.

Reverently lowering our eyes from the pillar of fire in Exodus and the unastronomical star in the East in St Matthew, we discover that flying altars were seen over the river Po in 222 BC and Pliny recorded flying shields scattering sparks in 100 BC. In the English port of Bristol in 1270, a spacecraft caught its anchor on a church steeple, but the pilot, who lowered a ladder to free it, asphyxiated in the earth's atmosphere and was quickly burned by the disturbed inhabitants. In the 1560s, black balls were profusely flying round the skies of Nürnberg and Basle, and the Reverend Cotton Mather, the Salem witches' snooper, in November 1668 observed in Boston a strange star within the horns of the moon.

The brilliance of Venus has beguiled many watchers into discovering that the stars, too, move across the sky. Comets were always fascinating, discernibly to the embroiderers of the Bayeux Tapestry. Edmond Halley saw the 1066 one return in 1682, and predicted its future visits. At seven in the morning on 6 March 1716, he found that he could read a book for two hours in the brightness of yet another strange object passing through the night sky. Electrical St Elmo's fire, sparkling on ships' spars and church spires in stormy weather, burning marshy methane gas creating will-o'-the-wisp, or ignis fatuus, or corpse candles in soggy graveyards, all illuminated mysteriously the uneasy heavens.

Flying saucers became sinisterly dignified as 'unidentified flying objects'. By 1966, 10,000 Americans had observed these UFOs, and had thus generated the even more ominous-sounding Air Force Scientific Advisory Board Committee to study them. The Russians were doing the same, though flying saucers had officially ceased to exist, via *Pravda*, in 1961. The US Air Force handed over the job to the University of Colorado, whose investigations took eighteen months and cost $300,000. The objects might have been crammed with Extra-terrestrial Persons, who were naturally a matter of professional concern to the US Air Force, though the wider view was expressed by a housewife giving them evidence: 'It would be so wonderfully exciting if it were true!'

Fifty-two per cent of American women believed in UFOs, against 43 per cent of men. Five per cent of Americans had seen one, but 87 per cent of those had not told anybody about it. UFOs were observed only by one or two people at a time, remaining strangely invisible, like the Loch Ness Monster, to the mass of passers-by. Nature added to the visual confusion with mirages, created by the refraction of light through unusual temperature gradients – since 1908, Loch Ness had recorded ships and mountaintops floating in the morning air as it began to lose its chill. Equally deceiving is the formation of lenticular clouds, which look like a pile of white crockery. Only a trivial 10 per cent of the American or British sightings could not be explained away as lies, hoaxes, and natural or man-made aerial phenomena.

An aeroplane being more obvious than a submarine, there were more photographs of UFOs than of Scotland's LNMs. They filled an issue of New York's popular magazine *Look* in 1967. Many of these UFOs were created by malfunctioning cameras, or by faulty negatives, or by sleight of hand. The larkers superimposed lamps on their pictures, or snapped spinning children's frisbees, or, more conveniently, a thread-suspended camera lens cap, or they simply photographed saucers. More practical enthusiasts created their own UFOs, from hot-air balloons made of plastic bags and birthday-cake candles. A patrolling Los Angeles security guard fired his revolver at daybreak at an invading UFO, but the bullets bounced off, and he became a national hero before correcting his report: he had shot a waterfront oil drum to break the monotony.

In 1807, President Thomas Jefferson scoffed at an idea of scientist Ernst Chladni of Wittenberg: 'I could more easily believe that two Yankee professors would lie than that stones would fall from heaven.' But Chladni was right. Stones *had* dropped from heaven. They were meteorites. The risk of our now sharing this unlucky presidential disbelief is slight. Solid evidence for the existence of UFOs is no more than some suspect or sketchy photographs. Equally so for the Loch Ness Monster, plus a short and ambiguous sonar sounding. The Yeti and Bigfoot have left only their fleeting footprints in the sands and snows of playtime.

Dismissal of such physical manifestations may be thought by Monster enthusiasts as cynical, and overwhelmed by the testimony of their being seen by reasonable numbers of normal human beings.

Unfortunately, this evidence is worthless.

A widespread human frailty is seeing things which are not there. There are three reasons for this:

61

– 1 *Physiological* The mechanism of human vision is infinitely more complicated than the mechanism of the most expensive cameras. Light is focused by our iris-ringed lens through the jelly of the eyeball upon the retina. This stimulates the optic nerves, which run backwards, meet on the base of the skull in the *optic chiasma*, then split, continue rearwards on their separate ways, and merge separately into the two sides of the brain.

The electrical impulses generated in the optic nerves – by our looking at anything from the remotest stars to our big toe – thus stimulate the cells of the occipital cortex. This lies at the back and base of the brain, at the spot where gentlemen's hatters insert little bows. We see out of the back of our heads.

The optic chiasma is a complicated junction. The visual traffic from the inner parts of both retinas crosses over, and so registers on the other side of the brain from where it started. The traffic from the outer parts of the retinas carries straight on, and so ends up on the same side of the brain.

Objects impacting from the outer parts of our visual fields are thus seen by the *opposite* half of the brain. Objects impacting from the inner parts of our visual fields are seen on the same half. A brain injury, from a blow to the back of the head, can bring *partial* blindness to *both* eyes. So can any disease which interrupts the optic nerve's path from the optic chiasma backwards. And we all know our 'floaters' – muscae volitantes, 'flitting flies' across the vitreous jelly filling our eyeballs, more of which swarm with short sight and old age.

– 2 *Psychological* What we see is far more elaborate than what we set eyes on.

Our brain is a soup of electrically charged chemicals which respond to stimuli, to perceptions and to anticipations. The brain modifies the impulses shooting backwards along the optic nerve to provide the visual image in our mind, as an electrically powered computer processes the information fed into it to produce an image on the screen. Vision gives us the clues; intelligence assembles the picture.

We approach our favourite armchair, noticing that it has two feet at the front. We see, from its familiar shape, that it has two more at the back, otherwise when we throw our slippered selves into it we should fall over backwards. Such perceptions are usually accurate enough to keep us out of danger or out of trouble, but sometimes they delude us. This is shown simply by some hackneyed optical illusions: the line flanked with outgoing chevrons looks longer than the same line with ingoing ones (this is dignified as the Muller-Lyer illusion); the three dark circles cut like cakes produce a nonexistent white triangle in the space between them.

The inside of a plaster mask of a human face is seen as an ordinary outward-looking face, because a hollow face is too improbable to be selected by the brain as a true perception. The identical image of a girl's flowing hair can become in another position a man's hand or a horse's tail. The retina sees no weight, but the weight of the bag we are about to lift, or the crumbs we are about to flick, is usefully inferred by the brain. The brain leaps at the immaterial from the material, like Walter Scott seeing the newly dead Byron in the plaids hanging in the hall at Abbotsford.

Seeing is *not* believing. It is believing what we see.

– 3 *Sociological*   A spouse who suffers from delusions often transmits them to the partner, and the couple then suffer cosily from *folie à deux*. The delusions enlarge their audience to the family and neighbours. They can spread across the village, like the delusions of malevolence from the witches of Salem; or across the world, like the belief in monsters or in flying bits and pieces. Do not we humans often feel inadequate? Lacking self-reliance? That the supernatural *still* threatens our existence? The menace of the Middle Ages sometimes overwhelms our sane judgment – perhaps gladly, because we cannot, and so need not, do anything to prevent the action of the uncontrollable. As Louis Pasteur warily warned scientists in 1854: 'The greatest derangement of the mind is to believe in something because one wishes it to be so.'

The auditory equivalent of UFOs impacted upon America on Sunday, 30 October 1938. Orson Welles broadcast a radio play about the Earth's invasion by Mars, and created a coast-to-coast panic such as gripped London in 1542, when the population fled from a fortune-teller's flood warning which happily went unfulfilled. The radio play was adapted from *The War of the Worlds*, the novel written in 1897 by H. G. Wells, who would appreciate having put the last word to monstrous apparitions in 1909:

> When ninety per cent out of the ten or twelve people one meets in a month not only say but feel and assume a thing, it is very hard not to fall into the belief that the thing is so.

## Things That Go Bump in the Night

With her head tucked underneath her arm
She walks the Bloody Tower!
With her head tucked underneath her arm
At the Midnight hour —
Song to Anne Boleyn, 1934

How attentive of the other world to entertain this one excitingly with its eternal visits. The ghosts who wander as a matter of course through Shakespeare display the antiquity of our shadowy belief in the returning dead, with their returning severed bodily parts, winding-sheets, everyday robes, underclothes, crowns, jewels, weapons, dogs, cats, horses, carriages, ships, tinder-boxes, writing materials and even insubstantial houses. Despite their immateriality, they are able to make their spectral presence forcibly felt by heavy footsteps, whispers, groans, shrieks, smells, chain-rattling, knockings, scratching on the woodwork and chucking things about.

The British have always taken ghosts seriously. In August 1631 at Durham, Mark Sharp and Christopher Walker were hanged at dawn, the day after their conviction for murdering farmer Walker's niece, aged seventeen, whom the farmer had got pregnant, solely on the evidence of her bloodstained ghost talking on four occasions to the local miller.

A famous London ghost walked in January 1762 in Cock Lane, near the Smithfield meat market. Miss Parsons, the twelve-year-old daughter of the haunted house, had often chatted to Miss Fanny, the mistress and sister-in-law of their lodger Mr Kent, whose wife had died in childbirth three years ago. And Miss Fanny herself had died two years ago, from smallpox, but she revealed hauntingly to the girl that her demise was really through poisoning by Mr Kent.

The Cock Lane house was suffering loud knockings and scratchings on the walls and doors all night, assaults that were confirmed by three intrepid clergymen. They too talked to Miss Fanny, through her servant Mary Frazer. Miss Fanny's ghost revealed that she had been poisoned in her purl – hot beer with gin, the 'dog's nose', taken early in the morning – and that her soul would lie at rest only when Mr Kent had confessed and was hanged for the crime. She added that he certainly would be within the next three years. Miss Fanny's answers to the clerics' questions were given by knocks on the wall, one for yes and two for no. Yes, she had told her servant Carrots an hour before dying that she had been poisoned; the living Carrots disagreed, but nobody wanted to spoil the show. At four in the morning, Miss Fanny gave four final knocks and went off to frighten the landlord of the Wheatsheaf pub next door.

So many Londoners jammed Cock Lane to see the ghost and hear the knocks that Mr Parsons – the parish clerk, who was being sued by Mr Kent for repayment of loans –

was obliged to charge admission. When the murdered woman made an appointment to knock on her coffin at midnight, the local socialites crammed into the Clerkenwell church vault. But Miss Fanny failed to turn up. Suspicion of playing japes fell upon the Parsons daughter, but so many enthusiasts had so fervently believed in the ghost, and would look so stupid were it human, that they explained away Miss Fanny's absence by asserting that Mr Kent had filched from the vault the guilty coffin.

So Mr Kent angrily opened the coffin, and there was Fanny. On 10 July, the Lord Chief Justice sent parish clerk Parsons to the pillory, and his wife and Mary Frazer to Bridewell prison, for conniving with the daughter over the scratching and knocking. 'That any contrivance so clumsy could have deceived anybody cannot fail to excite our wonder,' Charles Mackay summarises perceptively. 'But thus it always is. If two or three persons can only be found to take the lead in any absurdity, however great, there is sure to be plenty of imitators. Like sheep in a field, if one clears the stile, the rest will follow.'

Ten years later, a more noisy ghost projected fame across the Thames upon Vauxhall, when Mrs Golding on Twelfth Night had her cups and saucers crashing down the chimney, her pots and pans hurtling through the windows, her ham and cheeses whirling round the kitchen, her tables and chairs skidding across the floor. The poor woman and her maid Anne Robinson were sheltered by the neighbours, but the supernatural tumult hit them, too, and they shot her out again. Mrs Golding sacked Anne, and won peace. The maid confessed later to so delicately balancing the topping china, and so skilfully jerking items with horse-hairs, that she would have performed applausively as a juggler. It had seemed to her a useful way of clearing the house so she could have sex with her boyfriend.

Worse chaos occurred in 1838 in a Baldarroch farmhouse in Aberdeenshire. Domestic utensils whirled inside, farm implements and milk-churns outside; there were flying bricks, hay-ricks dancing to the Devil's bagpipes, and the boiling potatoes turning into demons, while the minister and elders of the Kirk devoutly prayed for preservation from the Devil. It was all done by the two servant-lassies, though the farmer's family puffed the story because they so enjoyed the passing importance. It was as exciting as today finding yourself unexpectedly on the telly. Our present poltergeists, too, are mostly ingenious youngsters who find it an enjoyable way to throw their weight about.

Ghostly nonsense is epitomised in the ludicrous story of Borley rectory, Britain's most profitably publicised leg-pull after the Loch Ness Monster.

Borley is an unnoticeable Suffolk village twenty miles inland across the flat fields from Ipswich. The twenty-three room, double-gabled rectory, with a fronting conservatory and upstairs chapel, was built in 1863 when Victorian architecture expressed solid family values (the rector, the Rev Henry Bull, had fourteen children). It was erected on the site of a thirteenth-century monastery (not really, they found in 1938). Once, a monk had fled with a novice from a nearby nunnery, but they were caught and killed for behaving so normally. Now the nun haunted the village, and so did their elopement coachman, without his head but with his coach. On a summer's evening in 1900, three of the Bull sisters saw the nun on the lawn.

In October 1928, the Rev Eric Smith moved into the rectory after it had been unoccupied – at least by humans – for sixteen months. His fretting over the local ghostly gossip inadvertently turned his home into an impregnable outpost of the supernatural. He wrote for advice to the *Daily Mirror*.

A reporter from London was down instantly, followed hotly by Harry Price. Price was a trained engineer, now the self-appointed director of the University of London Council for Psychical Investigation (which had nothing to do with London University). He was Foreign Research Officer of the American Society for Psychical Research, he wrote popular books about ghost-hunting, he was always in the newspapers and later on the wireless. The ghosts at Borley instantly started behaving badly, throwing stones, shattering windows, splintering the looking-glasses and frightening the maid. So many *Daily Mirror* readers came to see for themselves, the rector moved out.

In 1930, the next rector, the Rev Lionel Foyster, attracted ghosts as St Francis of Assisi attracted hungry birds. Two thousand spectral visits were recorded by the hastily summoned Harry Price, before a spiritualist group arrived to perform an emergency exorcism. The rector's wife, twenty-five years younger, went off with a Canadian widower who had got a black eye from a ghost during the night, and they opened a London flower shop.

Price himself rented the rectory in 1937, while writing *The Most Haunted House in England*. The rectory's lack of gas, electricity, central heating, and mains water testified to the supernatural enthusiasm of the investigators he invited to fill it at weekends. In so expectedly eventful surroundings, they entered a state of anxiety and suggestibility which aroused them to see and hear the other world better than this one.

If ghosts are expected to call in the still of the night, those familiar domestic creaks, knocks and gurgles which reach our insomniac ears become ghostly ones. The Borley rose bushes were known to tap the conservatory panes in the wind, the rectory was aswarm with scampering rats and mice, and Price's helpful hospitality to spectres was once embarrassingly discovered to involve filling his pockets with pebbles and bits of brick. A white-robed monk was at second glance the smoke from a bonfire, the headless spectre was the maid's boyfriend larking with his coat over his head, and the mysterious nocturnal lights in the windows were the fleetingly reflected carriages of the LNER. Borley rectory was not isolated, as Price suggested, but hard against a large farm with snorting pigsties and empty cottages, from which a woman's renowned supernatural moaning one night: 'Don't, Carlos, don't!' could have arisen with banal naturalness.

Harry Price brought Borley rectory worldwide fame, unaffected by its burning down on the night of 27 February 1939. During World War Two, digging in the ruins as earnestly as any air-raid squad, Price found a bit of skull and half a jaw. This was X-rayed by his dentist and diagnosed to come from a female harbouring a bony infection, which Price triumphantly matched to the painful expression habitually worn by the haggard returning nun.

Borley ghosts won fans in the most sagacious places. 'A very strong case has undoubtedly been put forward,' the Senior Master of the Supreme Court judged in the *Law Times* in 1941, 'and we are at a loss to understand what cross-examination of the witnesses could possibly shake it.' America's *Life* magazine photographers called just before D-Day (America is as thin on ghosts as on teatime crumpets), to be rewarded with a levitated brick, which could have been a suspended brick, like the UFO lens-caps. Price wrote another book on the rectory, before on 29 March 1948 joining his prey. The rectory ruins were demolished, but people came there for years afterwards to enjoy picnic seances.


### Things That Go Bump in the Afternoon

The first Principal of St Hugh's College in north Oxford, founded for women in 1886, was forty-year-old Charlotte

**69**

Anne Moberly, daughter of the Bishop of Salisbury and author of *Faith of the Prophets*. Miss Moberly retired in 1915 in favour of the Vice-Principal since 1902, Eleanor Frances Jourdain. Aged about fifty, daughter of the vicar of Ashburne, Miss Jourdain had read modern history at Lady Margaret Hall, had been a headmistress in Watford, was a Doctor of the University of Paris and the author of *Dramatic Theory and Practice in France 1690–1808*.

In 1901, Miss Jourdain had a flat in Paris, and Miss Moberly came across for a few weeks of the long vac. Paris was *en fête* for the International Exhibition – which created the delicious legend of the Vanishing Lady.

Surely you remember? An English officer's widow and her young daughter, returning home via Marseilles, arrived at the Hôtel Crillon in the Place de la Concorde. Mother felt ill, she summoned the hotel doctor, and the daughter was dispatched by the doctor across Paris to fetch some medicine. It was a long, crawling, hot drive in the *fiacre*, ended by the girl's return to the hotel and her discovery that she was utterly unkown to the same staff and to the shrugging doctor. She found no record of their arrival, their room long occupied, and, when she insisted on viewing it, entirely different. The girl reached England wondering if she were mad. The Crillon staff had been briefed, the register changed, the room redecorated, because mother had died swiftly of the Indian plague, the unhushed news of which would have emptied Paris of visitors overnight, and been terrible for business.

On the sunny, breezy Saturday afternoon of 10 August 1901, the highly unlegendary Miss Moberly and Miss Jourdain took a trip to Versailles, and after lunch wandered towards Marie-Antoinette's outlying château, the Petit Trianon. There they suddenly felt depressed. The wind suddenly dropped, and everything round them suddenly looked odd, 'as though painted on canvas'. They strolled on, past an idle plough, past a kiosk, through a grotto, asked directions from two green-uni-formed officials, were accosted by a running, breathless young man in a flying green cloak, were eyed sus-piciously by a pock-marked man in a big hat, noticed a lady sitting sketching, were sharply turned away by a man leaving the building and slamming the door, then found themselves among a pack of French tourists. Neither Miss mentioned all this to the other for a week.

Three months later, each Miss wrote an independent (and inconsistent) note of their *mauvais quart d'heure*. When Miss Moberly returned to the Trianon a few months later, on 2 January 1902, she was amazed to find no grotto, no kiosk, no ploughs, the buildings different, a new wall, fewer trees, no notable people. It struck her that they had previously wandered into 1789. On the 10 August of that year, the Tuileries was sacked by the Revolutionary mob.

For the next nine years, the Principal and Vice-Princi-pal huddled at St Hugh's to clothe their vision with historical flesh. What they saw, and what they did not see, the identity of those they met, the grotto (later demolished by Louis-Philippe), the vanished kiosk, the plough, were precisely confirmed by historical docu-ments of painstakingly pierced obscurity. Even the Tri-anon gardeners' wages books were dug out. Even twelve bars of the drifting, unknown tune from an invisible 1789 string band was identified through the Conservatoire de Musique de Paris, having been kept in Miss Jourdain's head for ten years. They even unearthed a picture of the Dauphin learning to plough.

In 1911, they published *An Adventure* about it. Miss Moberly was disguised as Elizabeth Morison, a tourist disclaiming any academic aptitude, and Miss Jourdain as Frances Lamont, a schoolmistress. It sold seven reprints in two years. The combination of English Misses, history and ghosts was irresistible. Everyone took it with intense seriousness, and all the documents now lodge in eternal glory in the Bodleian Library.

The Misses became so famous and enriched they could afford later to reveal themselves on the title-page. Just before World War Two, a spoilsport wrote an equally painstaking work noticing that bits of their 1901 accounts had been omitted from the 1911 book, and bits not in them inserted, and proved that the Misses' research was but an elaborate rationalisation for their seeing things which were not there.

As the Loch Ness Monster is often imagined in a floating log or a cloud-shadowed ripple or a rising trout, the two Misses – warm, tired, strolling into the shade of the trees – saw officials with staves for gardeners with spades, courtiers in visitors, and the Queen in an artistic tourist sitting on a camp-stool. Then they decorated their figments with enthusiastically excavated fossils from historical records. The more they researched, the more they believed in their own imaginations. So did the amazed public, always avid for a thrilling abnormal explanation rather than a boring normal one. It made as good a story as plague in the Crillon.

The Trianon adventure was possibly all a spoof to lighten the seriousness of high academic life. Miss Jourdain died in 1924, Miss Moberly in 1937, but perhaps we can catch them on a bright Oxford afternoon, in their fichu-draped bodices, flowing skirts and buttoned boots, pouring over eighteenth-century documents in the quad of St Hugh's.

Ghosts are manifested by somebody having a delusion or a jape. They swiftly attract a fan club of the credulous. Their irrepressible chill betters the funfair ghost train and horror movies. They award the ghostmaker with a profitable reputation. But perhaps they express less a menacing ghoulishness than the agreeable human frailty of enjoying a bit of fun.

# SIX

# Ghouls in Human Shape

The gawping crowd that collects round an even mildly gory accident exhibits, in its promptness, a frailty of mankind comparable to picking up other people's dropped banknotes.

The police repeatedly complain that motorway drivers mechanically slow down to view the remains of any spectacular collision, thus inviting fatal collision themselves by drivers speeding behind, and the creation of a second perilous distraction. A plane crash of sufficiently impressive mortality shortly jams the surrounding roads, and people bring their children.

## Hanging Matters

Such relish to view fellow humans' violent ends was being officially blessed in London on Monday, 20 July 1840:

> X——, who had voted with Mr Ewart for the abolition of the punishment of death, was anxious to see the effect on the public mind of an execution, and asked me to accompany him to see Courvosier killed. We had not the advantage of a sheriff's order, like the 'six

hundred noblemen and gentlemen' who were
admitted within the walls of the prison; but
determined to mingle with the crowd at the foot of the
scaffold, and take up our positions at a very early
hour.

As I was to rise at three in the morning, I went to
bed at ten, thinking that five hours' sleep would be
amply sufficient to brace me against the fatigues of the
coming day. But, as might have been expected, the
event of the morrow was perpetually before my eyes
through the night, and kept them wide open. I heard
all the clocks in the neighbourhood chime the hours
in succession; a dog from some court hard by kept up
a pitiful howling; at one o'clock, a cock set up a feeble
melancholy crowing; shortly after two the daylight
came peeping grey through the window-shutters; and
by the time that X—— arrived, in fulfilment of his
promise, I had been asleep about half-an-hour. He,
more wise, had not gone to rest at all, but had
remained up all night at the Club along with Dash and
two or three more. Dash is one of the most eminent
wits in London, and had kept the company merry all
night with jokes about the coming event. It is curious
that a murder is a great inspirer of jokes . . .

X——'s carriage has driven up to the door of my
lodgings, and we have partaken of an elegant *déjeuner*
that has been prepared for the occasion. A cup of
coffee at half-past three in the morning is
uncommonly pleasant; and X—— enlivens us with the
repetition of the jokes that Dash has just been making.
Admirable, certainly – they must have had a merry
night of it, that's clear; and we stoutly debate whether,
when one has to get up so early in the morning, it is
best to have an hour or two of sleep, or wait and go to
bed afterwards at the end of the day's work. The fowl
is extraordinarily tough – the wing, even, is as hard as
a board; a slight disappointment, for there is nothing
else for breakfast. 'Will any gentleman have some
sherry and soda-water before he sets out? It clears the
brains famously.' Thus primed, the party sets out. The
coachman has dropped asleep on the box, and wakes

up wildly as the hall-door opens. It is just four
o'clock . . .

The ginshop keepers have many of them taken their
shutters down, and many persons are issuing from
them pipe in hand. Down they go along the broad
bright street, their blue shadows marching *after* them;
for they are all bound the same way, and are bent like
us on seeing the hanging.

It is twenty minutes past four as we pass St
Sepulchre's: by this time many hundred people are in
the street, and many more are coming up Snow Hill.
Before us lies Newgate Prison; but something a great
deal more awful to look at, which seizes the eye at
once, and makes the heart beat, is –

There it stands, black and ready, jutting out from a
little door in the prison. As you see it, you feel a kind
of dumb electric shock, which causes one to stare a
little, and give a sort of gasp for breath. The shock is
over in a second; and presently you examine the
object before you with a certain feeling of complacent
curiosity. At least, such was the effect that the gallows
produced upon the writer, who is trying to set down
all his feelings as they occurred, and not to exaggerate
them at all.

After the gallows-shock had subsided, we went
down into the crowd, which was very numerous, but
not dense as yet. It was evident that the day's *business*
had not begun. People sauntered up, and formed
groups, and talked; the newcomers asking those who
seemed *habitués* of the place about former executions;
and did the victim hang with his face towards the
clock or towards Ludgate Hill? and had he the rope
round his neck when he came on the scaffold, or was
it put on by Jack Ketch afterwards? and had Lord
W—— taken a window, and which was he . . .?

The crowd has grown very dense by this time, it is
about six o'clock, and there is great heaving, and
pushing, and swaying to and fro; but round the
women the men have formed a circle, and keep them
as much as possible out of the rush and trample. In
one of the houses, near us, a gallery has been formed
on the roof. Seats were here let, and a number of

**75**

persons of various degrees were occupying them. Several tipsy dissolute-looking young men, of the Dick Swiveller cast, were in this gallery. One was lolling over the sunshiny tiles, with a fierce sodden face, out of which came a pipe, and which was shaded by long matted hair, and a hat cocked very much on one side. This gentleman was one of a party which had evidently not been to bed on Sunday night, but had passed it in some of those delectable night-houses in the neighbourhood of Covent Garden. The debauch was not over yet, and the women of the party were giggling, drinking, and romping, as is the wont of these delicate creatures; sprawling here and there, and falling upon the knees of one or other of the males. Their scarves were off their shoulders, and you saw the sun shining down upon the bare white flesh, and the shoulder-points glittering like burning-glasses . . .

Really the time passed away with extraordinary quickness. A thousand things of the sort related here came to amuse us. First the workmen knocking and hammering at the scaffold, mysterious clattering of blows was heard within it, and a ladder painted black was carried round, and into the interior of the edifice by a small side door. We all looked at this little ladder and at each other – things began to be very interesting. Soon came a squad of policemen; stalwart rosy-looking men, saying much for City feeding; well-dressed, well-limbed, and of admirable good humour . . .

But yonder, glittering through the crowd in Newgate Street – see, the Sheriff's carriages are slowly making their way. We have been here three hours! Is it possible that they can have passed so soon? Close to the barriers where we are, the mob has become so dense that it is with difficulty a man can keep his feet. Each man, however, is very careful in protecting the women, and all are full of jokes and good-humour. The windows of the shops opposite are now pretty nearly filled by the persons who hired them. Many young dandies are there with moustaches and cigars; some quiet fat family-parties, of simple honest tradesmen and their wives, as we fancy, who are looking on with the greatest imaginable calmness, and sipping their tea . . .

It was past seven now; the quarters rang and passed away; the crowd began to grow very eager and more quiet, and we turned back every now and then and looked at St Sepulchre's clock. Half-an-hour, twenty-five minutes. What is he doing now? He has his irons off by this time. A quarter: he's in the press-room now, no doubt. Now at last we had come to think about the man we were going to see hanged. How slowly the clock crept over the last quarter! Those who were able to turn round and see (for the crowd was now extraordinarily dense) chronicled the time, eight minutes, five minutes; at last – ding, dong, dong, dong! – the bell is tolling the chimes of eight.

\*    \*    \*

Between the writing of this line and the last, the pen has been put down, as the reader may suppose, and the person who is addressing him has gone through a pause of no very pleasant thoughts and recollections. The whole of the sickening, ghastly, wicked scene passes before the eyes again; and, indeed, it is an awful one to see, and very hard and painful to describe.

As the clock began to strike, an immense sway and movement swept over the whole of that vast dense crowd. They were all uncovered directly, and a great murmur rose, more awful, bizarre and indescribable than any sound I had ever before heard. Women and children began to shriek horribly. I don't know whether it was the bell I heard; but a dreadful quick feverish kind of jangling noise mingled with the noise of the people, and lasted for about two minutes. The scaffold stood before us, tenantless and black; the black chain was hanging down ready from the beam. Nobody came. 'He has been respited,' some one said; another said, 'He has killed himself in prison.'

Just then, from under the black prison-door, a pale quiet head peeped out. It was shockingly bright and distinct; it rose up directly, and a man in black appeared on the scaffold, and was silently followed by about four more dark figures. The first was a tall grave man: we all knew who the second man was. '*That's he – that's he!*' you heard the people say, as the devoted man came up.

I have seen a cast of the head since, but, indeed, should never have known it. Courvosier bore his punishment like a man, and walked very firmly. He was dressed in a new black suit, as it seemed: his shirt was open. His arms were tied in front of him. He opened his hands in a helpless kind of way, and clasped them once or twice together. He turned his head here and there, and looked about him for an instant with a wild imploring look. His mouth was contracted into a sort of pitiful smile. He went and placed himself at once under the beam, with his face towards St Sepulchre's. The tall grave man in black twisted him round swiftly in the other direction, and, drawing from his pocket a night-cap, pulled it tight over the patient's head and face. I am not ashamed to say that I could look no more, but shut my eyes as the last dreadful act was going on which sent this wretched guilty soul into the presence of God . . .

'The Lord giveth and the Lord taketh away,' – on a Monday morning, at eight o'clock, this man is placed under a beam, with a rope connecting it and him; a plank disappears from under him, and those who have paid for good places may see the hands of the Government agent, Jack Ketch, coming up from his black hole, and seizing the prisoner's legs, and pulling them, until he is quite dead – strangled . . .

I fully confess that I came away down Snow Hill that morning with a disgust for murder, but it was for *the murder I saw done*. As we made our way through the immense crowd, we came upon two little girls of eleven and twelve years: one of them was crying bitterly, and begged, for Heaven's sake, that someone would lead her from that horrid place. This was done, and the children were carried into a place of safety. We asked the elder girl – and a very pretty one – what brought her into such a neighbourhood? The child grinned knowingly, and said, 'We've koom to see the mon hanged!' Tender law, that brings out babes upon such errands, and provides them with such gratifying moral spectacles! . . .

That I can see Mr Ketch at this moment, with an easy air, taking the rope from his pocket; that I feel myself ashamed and degraded by the brutal curiosity which took me to that brutal sight; and that I pray to Almighty God to cause this disgraceful sin to pass from among us, and to cleanse our land of blood.

This applaudable prayer of William Makepeace Thackeray was answered on 26 May 1868, when English public executions became henceforth private.

François Benjamin Courvosier was the Swiss valet of Lord William Russell of Park Lane, though unhappy in his work. On the evening of 5 May 1840, Courvosier was sacked for forgetting to order the carriage and for muddling about with the warming-pan for his Lordship's bed. He shortly took a knife from the dining-room sideboard and crept upon his master, who was snoring by rushlight, murdered him, draped his towel over his face, found the keys of the Russian leather strong-box, stuffed the banknotes into his stockings and hid the double napoleons and the sovereigns in the watercloset off the back parlour. He then damaged the front door to suggest burglars and went to bed.

'Oh God! How could I have committed so dreadful a crime? It was madness. When I think of it I can't believe it,' Courvosier confessed in Newgate, where he feebly tried suicide. Many manservants had joined the 20,000 crowd at the execution. 'Jack Ketch' was then William Calcraft, himself a former butler, who 'slightly convulsed' his prisoner's legs two minutes after hanging him, completing the job.

The murder had packed Park Lane with fashionable crowds and claimed daily columns in *The Times*, which reported the agitation of the 'nobility and gentry who live in comparative seclusion'. Lord Russell was given a wonderful funeral at his estate in Rickmansworth, where that murderous May evening claimed a third casualty: 'We regret to state that the Rev M. Bowers, whilst descending into the vault, struck his head against a projecting stone, by which he received a severe contusion of the forehead.'

When Courvosier was hanged, there were 200 offences for which any man, woman or child could provide the same entertainment. These were lessened in 1832 by the dismissal of death for stealing horses, sheep or cattle, in 1835 for burglary and forgery, in 1841 for abusing children under ten, and in 1861 for setting fire to dwellings. Scotland had ceased turning a hanging into a performance two years earlier (the hangman was sometimes kilted for the job). Nobody in the Navy had been hanged from the yardarm since 13 July 1860, and that was on the Yangtze. In France, the last public guillotining occurred at 4.50 a.m. on 17 June 1939, at Versailles, and drew a full house. The Chinese used to cut off the ears, and strips of flesh, from men and women, and eat the fresh delicacies in front of the victims' eyes before executing them, but they stopped early in this century.

### The Compleat Hangman

The more elaborate gruesomeness of hanging followed by drawing and quartering was conceived by the English in 1241. The sentence was helpfully specific:

> That the traitor be dragged along the surface of the ground, tied to the tail of a horse, and drawn to the gallows and there hanged by the neck until he be *half* dead and then cut down; and his entrails be cut out of his body and burnt by the excutioner; then his head is to be cut off, his body to be divided into quarters, and

afterwards his head and quarters to be set up in some open places directed.

This technique was last exhibited at Derby in 1817. The gallows outside the jail was supplemented by a platform bearing a headsman's block, two axes, two sharp knives, a basket, and two sacks of sawdust for mopping up. The three traitors on show hung for half an hour before the second stage of the operation began. Cavalry with drawn swords were necessary to control the pressing mass of excited spectators, including Shelley. This time, the final quartering was omitted, by merciful order of the Prince Regent.

The public can become blasé about these enjoyments. Thackeray has another account, of Arthur Thistlewood and four of his fellow conspirators in the Cato Street plot – which was to murder the unlovable Foreign Secretary Viscount Castlereagh, and much of the Cabinet, while they were dining in Grosvenor Square. When the plotters were hanged and beheaded in 1820, the executioner held high the first head immediately after its severance, with the prescribed: 'Here is the head of a traitor!' This struck terror and disgust through the crowd. The second head created interest. The third raised little excitement. The fourth head, bloody and slippery, the executioner dropped. 'Ah, butter-fingers!' yelled the mob, roaring with laughter.

Even when secluded, a hanging provided a singular ceremony. In England, executions were held at eight o'clock, except at Wandsworth and Lincoln prisons, where it was at nine. Yorkshireman William Berry, who applied for the hangman's job in 1883 among 1,400 eager applicants, described in *My Experiences as an Executioner* the deadly procession which formed as the prison bell started tolling:

```
                    Chief Warder
        Warder                          Warder
                      Chaplain
           Warder  Convict  Warder
                     Executioner
        Principal Warder   Principal Warder
        Warder                          Warder
               Governor and Sheriff
             Wand Bearer    Wand Bearer
             Gaol Surgeon and Attendant
```

The chaplain added to the condemned man's gloom by ringingly conducting *en route* the burial service.

Mr Berry himself always entered the condemned cell punctually at 7.57 a.m., and revealed with admirable practicality:

> The pinioning arrangements, like the rest of the arrangements for an execution, are very simple. A broad leather body-belt is clasped round the convict's waist, and to this the arm-straps are fastened. Two straps, an inch and a half wide, with strong steel buckles, clasp the elbows and fasten them to the body-belt, while another strap of the same strength goes round the wrist, and is fastened to the body-belt in front. The legs are pinioned by means of a single two-inch strap below the knees. The rest of the apparatus consists of a white cap, shaped somewhat like a bag, which pulls down over the eyes of the criminal to prevent his seeing the final preparations . . .
>
> The alteration of which I speak is a little one suggested by myself, and consists of the substitution of a slope, or a level gangway, in place of steps. I have found, in some cases, when the criminals were nervous or prostrated, that the steps formed a practical difficulty. The slope, or gangway, was approved by the Home Office, and was first used on April 15th, 1890, at Kirkdale Gaol, for the execution of Wm. Chadwick. It was a simple improvement, but it has turned out to be a very useful one . . .
>
> The essential parts of the scaffold are few. There is

the heavy cross-beam, into which bolts terminating in hooks are usually fastened. In some cases this cross-beam stands on two upright posts, but usually its ends are let into the walls of the scaffold-house. Of course the hooks fastened to it are intended to hold the rope. The scaffold proper, or trap, or drop, as it is variously called, is the portion of the structure to which most importance is attached, and of which the Government furnishes a plan. It consists of two massive oaken doors, fixed in an oak frame-work on a level with the floor, and over a deep, bricked pit. The arrangement is a very good one; as both doors must necessarily fall at exactly the same moment. Their great weight – for they are of three-inch oak – causes them to drop very suddenly, even without the weight of the criminal, and they are caught by spring catches to prevent any possibility of rebound.

With pencil and paper Mr Berry had already made each fatal morning's vital calculation. He complained:

It is, of course, necessary that the drop should be of sufficient length to cause instantaneous death, that is to say, to cause death by dislocation rather than by strangulation; and on the other hand, the drop must not be so great as to outwardly mutilate the victim. If all murderers who have to be hanged were of precisely the same weight and build it would be very easy to find out the most suitable length of drop, and always give the same; but as a matter of fact they differ enormously.

Mr Berry got £5 a drop.

The hangman's rope now hangs impotently in the Black Museum in Scotland Yard. It is only four feet long, an inch thick, the top end encompassing a bright brass collar three inches across, for connection to the cross-beam hook. The business end is bound in shiny leather, forming a noose by a small brass ring secured with a tight leather washer, of which Mr Berry was the innovator, and always positioned behind the left ear.

A man or woman being killed invisibly at breakfast-time still brought crowds to the prison gates. The only evidence of what was going on inside came from the tolling prison bell, though when Hawley Harvey Crippen of Hilldrop Crescent was hanged at Pentonville Prison on 24 November 1910 for the murder of his wife, the clapper stayed mute out of official solicitude for three other prisoners awaiting shortly the same procedure.

The watchers pressed, wide-eyed, towards the black-framed notice, signed by the prison governor, the under-sheriff and the chaplain, which appeared outside the prison gate to announce that the deed was done. It was soon the only trace of the fascinating event. The body hung an hour, the post-mortem was promptly performed, the inquest was held, and by noon the convict would be in quicklime. The current popularity of capital punishment in the United States, giving the prisoner the benefit of the latest scientific lethal techniques, has revived a zestful ghoulishness observable outside the prison, in the newspapers and on television.


### O horror! horror! horror!

Judicial flogging was conducted with the same unchanging ceremony as hanging.

Private Somerville of the Scots Greys has left an account of this spectacle, occurring two years after Thackeray's chilling experience, but seen from the inside.

Somerville was court-martialled for refusing to remount his horse and sentenced to 200 lashes, which he got the same afternoon. The regiment formed up four deep round the walls of the riding school, the officers within the oblong, all to relish the essential punishment for disobeying orders. The regimental surgeon and three hospital orderlies were in attendance, and the sergeant of the regimental band had the *green bag* containing the cats.

There were four whips, in case one or more broke at their task. The wood or whalebone handles were two feet long, as were the nine whipcord tails with six knots each. Somerville was read the minutes of the court martial and roped firmly to a ladder, and the sergeant-major took out his pencil to count the strokes. On his command: 'Farrier Simpson, you will do your duty,' the soldier swung the cat-o'-nine-tails twice round his head, gave the stroke, and drew the tails through his fingers to rid them of skin, blood or flesh. This was the regimental drill. After calling out the receipt of twenty-five lashes, the sergeant-major ordered, 'Halt!' and a regimental trumpeter continued with the cat until fifty up, when the farrier resumed. After a hundred, the colonel called off the attack.

'I felt my flesh quiver in every nerve, from the scalp of my head to my toe-nails,' remembered the victim. 'The time between each stroke seemed so long as to be agonising, and yet the next came too soon . . . I felt as if I would burst in the internal parts of my body. I detected myself once giving something like a groan, and to prevent its utterance again I put my tongue between my teeth, held it there, and bit it almost in two pieces. What with the blood from my tongue and my lips, which I had also bitten, and the blood from my lungs or some other internal part ruptured by the writhing agony, I was almost choked, and became black in the face.'

He was unfastened, a wet towel was spread over his back, and he was taken to hospital.

The ghoulishness of human beings is loosed excitingly by revolutions. On 14 July 1789, M. de Launay, the governor of the Bastille, was being conducted by its liberators (whom he had politely stood an early lunch) to the nearby Hôtel de Ville. He was attacked from behind by François-Felix Dénot, an out-of-work cook. In the struggle, M. de Launay kicked him in the balls, which incited the mob to fall on the captive governor and drag him away from his military escort.

'He hurt you. Cut off his head,' advised one of the excited mob, handing Dénot a sabre. But the cook, finding himself unskilled with the sword, took from his pocket the knife he used for cutting up the roasts, and painstakingly and professionally removed M. de Launay's head. Dénot stuck it on a pitchfork, and it continued on its way to the Hôtel de Ville, a singing crowd behind. The cook left it overnight (against a receipt) with the captain of the guard at the Châtelet, and continued to parade it for a couple more days, until it became unserviceable, when he chucked it down the drain. Dénot refused money offered him by a *député*, saying that he had performed the carvery out of patriotism.

In Dijon, a 61-year-old counsellor was killed by sticks thrust down his throat and into his ears by his political opponents, who were later complimented by the judge. At Valence, an artillery captain was stabbed and shot in a church where he had fled to protest his innocence; officially, he was killed 'illegally but justly'. At Aix-en-Provence, under the eyes of the guarding soldiers, a frenzied mob hung from the trees a lawyer and two aristocrats. The lynchers were commended as 'bloody patriotic' in the forthright Revolutionary journal *Le Père Duchesne*, which afforded their victims the grudging funeral oration: 'They buggered off into the *vitam aeternam*! Wouldn't they have done better to have stayed where they were and quietly learned about the rights of man?'

In Nantes, Jean Baptiste Carrier, *représentant* at the National Convention, efficiently drowned in the Loire by night ninety priests in a flat-bottomed *gabarre*, for which he had devised special valves for quick sinking. 'The sentence of deportation was executed vertically,' Carrier noted wittily. The *gabarre* became a popular craft. The women passengers were stripped naked and their children thrown in after them: 'Wolflings who would grow to be wolves,' their executioners noted warily. The scuttling method was later considered uneconomical, so the prisoners were simply tied up and tossed in the river and shot if they swam. Some for diversion were tied in sexual pairs in the famous *mariage républicain*. Carrier, *trop zélé*, killed in *les noyades* during four months of 1793 some 15,000 inhabitants of La Vendée.

In Paris in September 1792, the Princess de Lamballe, a friend of Marie Antoinette so close that she was popularly believed to be her lesbian partner, was brought out of the medieval keep of the Temple, where she was imprisoned with the King, the Queen and their two children, and delivered to the mob. A single stroke of a sabre from behind removed her head. This was stuck on a pike, and was bobbed up and down outside the Queen's windows. The body was then dragged through the streets by a crowd of men and women excited to madness by their privilege to shed blood. The Princess's ripped clothes were cut off, and her executioner's sabre sliced away her breasts. He then carefully cut away her vulva and applied her pubic hair to his upper lip as a moustache. This had the crowd falling about. While carving the Princess's genitalia, the executioner had exclaimed jovially: 'The whore! No one is ever going to thread his way into her again!' The episode was officially commended as 'the stern justice of the people'.

O liberty! O liberty! what voluptuous ghoulishness is committed in thy name.

Louis XVI and Marie Antoinette starred in the royal performance *Grand Guignol* of the Place de la Révolution in 1793.

The earnest ghoulishness of the Nazis lies too light on history to need description. Its ten top instigators – lacking Hermann Goering, who two hours earlier had bitten into a smuggled cyanide capsule – at 1.11 a.m. on 16 October 1946 enjoyed in Nuremberg prison the civilising change in public attitudes by being hanged in private.

Human ghouls are now reduced to watching dramatised surgical operations. This frailty antedated television. Wrote an Edwardian traveller:

> It happened that I had been commanded to dine at Potsdam on August 26, 1902. In the course of the afternoon of that day, when driving in Berlin, I noticed large posters inviting the public to visit a waxworks exhibition with, among other things, life-size figures representing the various stages of the operation which King Edward had recently undergone at immanent peril to his life. Soldiers and children were admitted at half-price. The details had better not be described. It was a loathsome sight.

# SEVEN

# Cult Figures

The recurrent human frailty of believing any attractive idea, however ludicrous, grows strong in binding the crowd which it sweeps. Everyone becomes united in the conviction that, if everyone else believes something, he must be right in believing it, too. Like the right price for tulips.

### Tulipomania

The tulip, which joyously raises a vivid cup to newborn spring in countless suburban gardens, was transplanted to Europe in the mid-sixteenth century from Turkey. Konrad von Gesner MD, Professor of Natural History at Zurich, classifier of the whole world's animals in his vast *Historia Animalium* of 1558, the botanist who collected five hundred plants unknown to the Greeks and Romans, the keen mountaineer who died of the plague aged forty-nine in 1565, first observed them in 1559 resembling red lilies in a Bavarian garden. The bulbs had come from Constantinople, whose cultivators were delighted to supply more to such wealthy gardeners in Germany and Holland as were attentive to Professor von Gesner's authoritative admiration.

They did not come cheap.

The tulip before 1500 was a wild flower glowing in the winter sunshine of Turkey, Persia and India, which achieved mention in *Omar Khayyám*:

> As then the Tulip from her morning sup
> Of Heav'nly Vintage from the soil looks up . . .

Tamed into cultivation, they were spotted by the ambassador to the Sultan of Holy Roman Emperor Ferdinand I, on his way to Constantinople in 1554: 'not without great astonishment on account of the time of the year, as it was then the middle of winter, a season unfriendly to flowers . . . they have little or no smell, but are admired for their beauty and variety of colour. I received several presents of these flowers, which cost me not a little.' Later, the tulip was observed by a travelling Englishman as a Persian sex symbol – its scarlet petals were the lover's fire, its black base his burnt-out heart.

When the Ottoman Empire was ruled by Selim the Sot in 1566, the tulip became a national emblem like the English rose and Irish shamrock, appearing widely on china and drapery. The Turks turned for a while from tulips to cultivating succulent cucumbers and melons; but at the beginning of the eighteenth century, the reign of Sultan Ahmed III (the one who signed the peace of Passarowitz, which ended the war with Austria and unleashed the vampires of Transylvania) was decorated by history as 'the Age of Tulips'.

Sultan Ahmed maintained a flashy court, which presented regular tulip fêtes, stage-managed by the Grand Vizier. These spectacles were musical banquets, held by night amid flowerbeds and trellises crammed with multicoloured tulips, these illuminated by myriad lanterns and mirrors and enlivened by cages of canaries. There were more tulips massed into vivid pyramids, arches and patterned carpets. The Sultan feasted with his five wives and all his concubines and his chief coffee-maker. The grower of the finest blooms was ceremoniously honoured with a decorative diploma, which commanded his fellow horticulturists to offer him their appropriate respects: the deference of the closed-lip rosebud and the perfume-seeping hyacinth, and the humility of the bowed-head violet.

The next Ottoman Emperor, Mahmud I, held private tulip fêtes in his seraglio courtyard. A cannon shot signalled the flung-open doors of the harem, a thousand eunuchs emerged with scented torches, then a rush of liberated women fell upon the tulips in shrill delight. All were trying to catch the Sultan's eye, so that the Mistress of the Harem might wind up the party by presenting her with the Sultan's handkerchief, indicating that she was the blossom he had picked for the night. It makes the Chelsea Flower Show as prosaic as the municipal flowerbeds.

The bulb of a shapely and colourful tulip from Persia then made 1,000 pieces of gold in Constantinople. Half a million tulips sprouted extravagantly in the Palace gardens, which ordered them 50,000 at a time. The Turks enjoyed 1,300 varieties, with names like Lover's Dream, Fresh Breeze and Heart Reviver. The tulip has been called the peacock of flowers: 'the one has no scent, the other no song; the one glories in its gown, the other in its train'. Had tulips a fragrance matching in esteem their appearance, all the perfumes of Arabia would in comparison have smelt like disinfectants.

In 1570, cargoes of tulip bulbs started arriving in Antwerp from Constantinople. Tulips quickly became a social necessity for the moneyed Dutchman of taste, their fashionable roots inevitably descending into the merchant and shopkeeping classes. In France, the tulip appeared in Provence in 1611, and supplanted diamonds for *la femme décolletée*. In Germany, they tried cultivating them as vegetables.

The bulbs remained rare, the price of social esteem high and steadily mounting. By 1635, Admiral Van der Eyck was going for 1,200 florins a plant, and Admiral Liefken for 4,400. Many bulbs were stolen, the thieves swelling the booty by planting the seeds, though they took five years to flower. The tulip seeds – and, uniquely among flowers, the bulbs – sometimes produced mutations with colours never seen before. Everyone grew excited about this.

Each new variety of tulip was impressively named, eruditely criticised, excitedly chatted about, and launched amid the toasting of free wine, like the modern publication of a best seller. The red, white and blue Semper Augustus was the hit of Holland in 1623, selling for 3,000 florins (which was in England £300, when in London £240 was a top yearly salary). The prices of all tulip bulbs started rising ridiculously, and between 1634 and 1637 flew into the nonsensical. One Viceroy was swapped for 2 loads of wheat, 4 of rye, 4 fat oxen, 8 fat pigs, 12 fat sheep, 2 hogsheads of wine, 4 barrels of beer, 2 barrels of butter, 1,000 pounds of cheese, a bed, a suit of clothes and a silver beaker. A Semper Augustus was then fetching 4,600 florins plus 'a new and well made carriage and two dapple grey horses and all accessories'. A pair of roots bought twelve acres of building land in Amsterdam. The mania of *Tulpenwoede* had struck.

The passion for tulips was so firm a strand of human life, it occurred to no human that this filament might have an end to it. Nobles and their footmen, maids and chimney-sweeps, sailors and washerwomen, all played the tulip market. High- and low-priced tulips were specially grown for the convenient gambling of both rich and poor. You did not need to buy a whole tulip: just a half- or a quarter-share in a bulb. The gentry sold their houses, the farmers sold their land – for prices of which the stupidity was quickly forgotten in the rise of their floral investments – and workmen sold the tools they lived by.

When tulip prices wilted, the nurserymen bought; when the price shot up again, they sold. The customer paid for a bulb, raised from the earth in June, for delivery in time for autumn planting, when he took his profit or paid his loss. The deals were struck in taverns, stoutly sealed with food and drink, until the trade was officially regulated and the tulip-notary became the most important figure in the town. More conveniently, tulip markets were later appended to the stock exchanges of Amsterdam and Rotterdam, so that you could make your money without the bother of handling or even seeing its roots.

The rich of the world would continue to send to Holland for tulips, and pay whatever anyone cared to ask, because they could assuredly sell them at home for more. Antwerp would effortlessly become the world's wealthiest city. Holland contemplated the approaching total abolition of poverty as proudly as President Hoover later foresaw it for America. The cult of tulipomania makes a floral tribute to the New York Stock Exchange of 1929.

There were victims. A sailor delivering some oriental silks in Amsterdam was tipped by the merchant with a juicy pickled herring for his breakfast, which he embellished by pocketing an onion lying about the warehouse, and enjoyed both sitting on a bollard in the sunshine of the quay. The onion was a Semper Augustus, its disappearance creating the uproar of a vanished Rembrandt. The alarmed merchant searched frenziedly among his bales until, remembering the sailor, he rushed to the docks and found him savouring the last peelings from the tip of his claspknife. The meal 'might have sumptuously feasted the Prince of Orange and the whole court', bewailed the merchant, who had the sailor tried for felony and jailed for months.

The same accident afflicted an English botanist, who infuriated his Dutch host by curiously slicing an odd onion found in the conservatory. It was an Admiral Van der Eyck, for which the going rate was 4,000 florins. The mania predictably provoked an anti-tulip movement, led by the professor of botany at Leyden, who fell furiously with his walking-stick upon every tulip he encountered.

A single bulb of a prize French tulip was accepted as the price of a mill, another for a brewery (it was renamed Tulipe Brasserie). England was more cagey. According to Addison later in *The Tatler*, most Englishmen avoided resembling the typical sufferer: 'a very plain honest man, and a person of good sense, had not his head been touched with that distemper which Hippocrates calls the Tulippomania; insomuch that he would talk very rationally on any subject in the world but a tulip'.

The first bulbs reached London from Vienna in 1578. Fifty years later, the English nation of garden-potterers had 140 varieties to plant, all admired for their colours and stateliness. James I's herbalist advised that the bulbs be arranged with 'one colour answering and setting off another, that the place where they stand may resemble a piece of curious needle-worke, or piece of painting'. The English found that a tulip bulb in red wine was good for a crick in the neck and as an aphrodisiac. With clubbable English enthusiasm, a National Tulip Society was established in 1849.

In 1636, everyone in Holland with a yard or so of garden was growing tulips. Then it abruptly struck the Dutch that the price of tulips must fall like their petals in the brightening spring sunshine. Greater agricultural consumption causes greater production and plunging prices. It had already happened with asparagus in Göttingen. Realism spread as rapidly as the euphoria. As nobody wanted to be the last to sell, the market collapsed in panic. Growers found themselves with no money, only a few ugly spheres of worthless vegetable matter.

Furious pressure groups were formed, but the Governors of Holland and West Friesland refused to help, as the British Government disregarded the resentful ruined names at Lloyd's 350 years afterwards. Later, they agreed to annul contracts made before 1637, when tulipomania had raged at its most extravagant. Then the Provincial Council at The Hague deliberated a solution, but after three months gave up. Some vendors vanished with their takings. Others sued the buyers for the agreed price of the devalued bulbs, but the judges indicated that gambling debts were unrecoverable by law. In the end, everyone settled grumblingly for what they could get. The rocketing economy of tulipomania left nothing behind except its inflation. But the Dutch continued to love the flower which had ruined them. In 1836, Citadel of Antwerp fetched £650. And in London in 1835, Mrs Fanny Kemble, our sensational Shakespearian Juliet, went as a tulip for £75.

### The Flagellants

We frail humans are equally liable to suffer from epidemics of delusions as of diseases. In the fifteenth to seventeenth centuries, unwelcome disturbances of the environment, or of the body, were ascribed to the witches on broomsticks riding the moonlit, cloud-scudded night. In the thirteenth century, the streets day and night saw long processions of near-naked men, trailing behind priests bearing crosses and banners and singing psalms and ringing bells, the marchers howling their prayers, weeping and groaning, a candle in one hand and with the other flagellating themselves bloody with whips, rods, leather thongs and besom brooms. Women did it at home.

Such a painful progression began with the Egyptians, who beat their own backs at the yearly festival of Isis, the supreme goddess, daughter of the earth and sky. The Christians embraced self-flagellation as an effective and obvious form of penance, which by the eleventh century had become fashionable throughout the monasteries of Europe. In 1057, the vigour of the flagellants was commendably recorded by Cardinal Damian of Ostia, himself a zealous practitioner of the whip and a strict churchman who castigated bishops for playing chess. His hobby was carving wooden spoons.

The Franciscans were enthusiastic flagellants from their foundation by St Francis of Assisi in 1209. Their inspiring preacher St Antony of Padua zestfully took the whip hand by 1220. St Francis himself in 1212 met the eighteen-year-old noblewoman Clara Seiffo of Assisi, who like him had been a difficult child necessitating the regular birch. She had swooned over one of his sermons, and having begged an audience was directed to dress in penitential sackcloth and beg alms for the poor. Then she had to appear attired as a bride at the order's Portiuncula chapel, where St Francis sheared off her hair and slipped her into the Franciscan habit. Afterwards, they enjoyed a satisfying mutual-scourging relationship and she ended up a saint.

By the middle of the thirteenth century, flagellant groups were forming across the north of Italy like the clusters of sexual deviants of varying oddity collecting everywhere today. The cult leapt the Alps to the Rhine and Bohemia, after making such a nuisance of itself in Italy that the magistrates expelled its performers from their streets.

Flagellants then vanished, until the Black Death of 1346 provided an impotent terror which grasped at any activity that offered the hope of keeping alive. Men and women flagellating themselves and each other returned on the Danube and beat across the Rhine to the Low Countries. They flogged their way to Avignon to confront Pope Clement VI, who in 1349 had issued a bull proscribing their peculiarity as heresy, after which many were burnt at the stake and the rest frightened out of their whips.

To the irritation of the Inquisition, the notion of marching flagellation as the road to salvation spread again from Germany in 1414. It persisted in rakish Henri III of France, a keen scourger, who founded the White Penitents in March 1585 with a gorgeous procession of everybody important flagellating from the Augustine convent to Notre Dame (if unfortuntely it rained heavily). The King's succeeding processions were augmented by noble ladies shamelessly in their shifts. *Père conscrit des blancs battus*, they were calling him in Paris. Henri III's mother, Catherine de' Medici, whipped her court ladies behind locked doors. Nobles and other kings did it – England's Henry II had been scourged at the altar of Canterbury Cathedral in 1174 for the murder of Thomas à Becket – and numerous incipient saints flogged themselves naked all Lent, while chanting their way through the Psalter.

> It was long debated whether flagellation as a punishment or flagellation as a penance was the more ancient of the two kinds of whipping; but there need be little doubt about the matter: corporal *punishment* being old as sin,

wrote the Rev William M. Cooper BA, in *A History of the Rod* of 1869.

The Spartans had flogged their children until they bled. In the Peloponnese, women were flogged in the temple of Dionysus. Roman ladies beat their slaves:

> Woe to her waiting woman: the dressing-maids lay
> down their tunics: the straps break on the back of
> some; others redden under the lash of the leather
> scourge, and others of the twisted parchment,

recorded Juvenal in the first century.

The cult and the punitive custom are twin lashes on the same mysterious wand. Flagellation was a punishment performed on naughty Christian priests and monks by bishops. Self-flagellation was similarly the punishment of the zealously devout, for the sins that only they knew they had committed: Crusader Peter the Hermit in 1096 felt sexy towards a young woman he had saved from an officer's seduction, so he flagellated his back severely, after locking himself up with her mother. Confessors who imposed the penance of self-flagellation slipped into imposing the flagellation themselves, with more agreeable righteousness upon females.

In 1195, twenty-year-old St Edmund of Abingdon, later Archbishop of Canterbury, who was taking an arts course in Paris after coming down from Oxford, found himself tormentingly enticed by a lovely girl, for which forwardness he summoned her to his study, stripped her, and beat her, covering her body with weals. Capuchin Brother Matthew of Avignon woke to discover a girl in his bedroom, and beat her on the spot. Brother Bernardin was invited in by a Siena housewife, who made violent sexual advances upon him, to which he responded, and then, luckily having his scourge on him at the time, whipped her for both their sins. 'She loved the holy man the better afterwards; and so did her husband when he knew how things had been transacted.'

Of Carmelite St Theresa in 1562:

> Her chief delight was in flagellation. She would have
> given her life to scourge the whole world, or that the

whole world might scourge her, for she delighted alike in the infliction and the reception of the birch.

St Theresa whipped her bare-backed nuns until they bled, after which they had to thank her and kiss the hem of her habit, but they were given their own choice of implement from the birch-store. The Benedictine Order of Fontevrault, founded in 110 by Robert of Arbrissel, had fifty-seven unisex monasteries in France and three in England. All ruled by abbesses, they housed 300 nuns and 200 monks, meeting officially only in the church:

> Although the nuns flagellated each other, they greatly preferred to apply the birch to the monks and novices, who sometimes complained of their zeal to the abbess, who gave them another whipping.

Jesuit Father Gerard in 1728 held whipping soirées for his female disciples in Toulon. His favourite sinner was lovely, hysterical, 25-year-old Catherine Cadiere. He ordered: 'You should now undress yourself and be chastised; certainly you have deserved that the whole earth should be witnesses thereof, yet the gracious God has permitted that only I and this wall, which cannot speak, remain as witnesses.' Beating progressed to copulation, she later confessed, and produced his passionate letters. But the Jesuits rallied round and Catherine was tried for slander and imprisoned, whereupon the mob turned furiously upon Father Gerard. He shortly died; she vanished.

> *Cette belle voit Dieu, Gerard voit cette belle,*
> *Ah! Gerard est plus heureux qu'elle,*

commented Voltaire.

Possibly these episodes of erotic evangelism taken from

*A History of the Rod*, which was published by flagellant specialist John Hotton of Piccadilly, are as inexact as the respectability of its author, who was not the Rev William M. Cooper BA at all, but a Mr J. G. Bertram.

# EIGHT

# Lady Tinglebum

The flagellant cult lashed its way sporadically through succeeding centuries. They were still performing it in processions at Lisbon in 1820. At the same time, Mrs Berkley was doing it at 28 Charlotte Street, London, but that was for fun and you had to pay.

### Pain and Pleasure

*Le vice anglais* was established in *la vie française* by the nineteenth century as a bizarre English frailty. But an early enthusiast was the conceiver of liberty, equality and fraternity, Jean-Jacques Rousseau.

> Since Mlle Lambercier treated us with a mother's love, she had also a mother's authority, which she exercised sometimes by inflicting on us such childish chastisements as we had earned,

Rousseau began in his *Confessions*, which were written in 1766 at Wootton in Staffordshire. Aged eight, he had boarded with the thirty-year-old spinster schoolmistress near Geneva:

But when in the end I was beaten I found the
experience less dreadful in fact than in anticipation;
and the very strange thing was that this punishment
increased my affection for the inflicter.

He noticed that the pain and shame of being whipped
on his bare buttocks was sensual; so did Mlle Lambercier,
who declared abruptly that she found whipping exhaust-
ing, and banned him from sleeping in her room (in
winter, in her bed). Thereafter, flagellation fantasies filled
Rousseau's mind whenever he 'feasted feverish eyes on
lovely women'. But the most he dared achieve practically
was: 'to fall on my knees before a masterful mistress, to
obey her commands, to have to beg for her forgiveness',
which he found 'the most delicate of pleasures'.

Sexual polymath the Marquis de Sade was a diligent
flagellator. Aged twenty-two in the summer of 1763, he
invited home twenty-year-old Mlle Jeanne Testard (from
Mme de Rameau's reliable Paris brothel) to a room draped
in black, with four birches and five whips at the ready,
but she declined to co-operate. Next summer, Sade transferred his patronage to Mme Le Brissault's brothel, and
engaged four girls all together, whom he flogged naked,
then took out to dinner. In the spring of 1768, the Marquis
hired thirty-year-old pastrycook's widow Rose Keller to
do his housework, and when she arrived for duty he
stripped her, tied her hand and foot face downwards to
the bed, removed his coat and birched her until she
screamed. He then brought her *daube de boeuf* and
cognac for dinner, but she knotted the blankets, escaped
through the window and summoned the *gendarmerie*.
The Marquis was jailed, but for sacrilege, the carnal
performance having occurred on Easter Day.

In June 1772 at Marseilles, the Marquis flogged four
girls at once with a cat-o'-nine-tails, had them flog him,
then rang the sexual changes with the assistance of his

valet, who was dressed as a sailor. He philosophised that Nature provided sexual urges which we should satisfy, however odd they might appear to others. For this extravaganza, Sade was executed in September at Aix-en-Provence, but in effigy. Early in 1784, he was imprisoned in the Bastille, where he benefited from the *événements* of 14 July 1789, and became a judge in the court established by the Committee of Public Safety to try counterfeiters. There was good to be found in Citizen Sade. He always fed the ones he flogged. He died in Charenton asylum in 1814, aged seventy-six and copulating, to the last, with a fifteen-year-old laundress.

And Madame du Barry loved watching girls whipped.

In England, robust entertainment was provided by 'posture molls', who went to parties as strippers and both flogged or were flogged, though they were respectable women who never copulated for cash. Hogarth's harlot of 1730 has the birch hanging conveniently above her while she is enjoying breakfast in bed. In 1748, John Cleland created the Titania of the whip, Fanny Hill:

> Mr Barvile stood up near the fire, whilst I went to
> fetch the instruments of discipline out of a closet hard
> by: these were several rods, made each of two or three
> strong twigs of birch tied together, which he took,
> handled, and viewed with as much pleasure as I did
> with a kind of shuddering presage.
>
> Next we took from the side of the room a long broad
> bench, made easy to lie at length on by a soft cushion
> in a calico-cover: and everything now being ready, he
> took his coat and waistcoat off and, at his motion and
> desire, I unbuttoned his breeches and, rolling his shirt
> up rather above his waist, tucked it securely there.
> When directing naturally my eyes to that humoursome
> master-movement, in whose favour all these
> dispositions were making, it seemed almost shrunk
> into his belly, scarce showing its tip above the sprout

of hairy curls that clothed those parts, as you may have seen a wren peep its head out of the grass.

Stopping then to untie his garters, he gave them me for the use of tying him down to the legs of the bench, a circumstance no farther necessary than, as I suppose, it made part of the humour of the thing, since he prescribed it to himself, amongst the rest of the ceremonial.

I led him then to the bench, and according to my cue, played at forcing him to lie down: which, after some little show of reluctance, for form's sake, he submitting to, was straightway extended flat upon his belly on the bench, with a pillow under his face; and as he thus tamely lay, I tied him slightly hand and foot, to the legs of it; which done, his shirt remaining trussed up over the small of his back, I drew his breeches quite down to his knees; and now he lay, in all the fairest, broadest display of that part of the back-view in which a pair of chubby, smooth-cheeked and passing white posteriors rose cushioning upwards from two stout, fleshful thighs, and, ending their cleft, or separation, by a union at the small of the back, presented a bold mark that swelled, as it were, to meet the scourge.

Seizing now one of the rods, I stood over him, and, according to his direction, gave him, in one breath, ten lashes with much good will and the utmost nerve and vigour of arm that I could put to them, so as to make those fleshy orbs quiver again under them, whilst he himself seemed no more concerned, or to mind them, than a lobster would a flea-bite. In the meantime, I viewed intently the effects of them, which to me at least appeared surprisingly cruel: every lash had skimmed the surface of those white cliffs, which they deeply reddened, and lapping round the side of the furthermost from me, cut, especially into the dimple of it, such livid weals as the blood either spun out from or stood in large drops on; and from some of the cuts I picked out even the splinters of the rod, that had stuck in the skin; nor was this raw work to be wondered at, considering the greenness of the twigs, and the severity of the infliction, whilst the whole surface of his skin was so smooth-stretched over the hard and firm pulp of flesh that filled it as to yield no play or elusive swagging under the stroke, which thereby took place the more plum, and cut into the quick.

I was, however, already so moved at the piteous sight that I from my heart repented the undertaking, and would willingly have given over, thinking he had full enough: but he, encouraging and beseeching me earnestly to proceed, I gave him ten more lashes, and then resting, surveyed the increase of bloody appearances, and at length, steeled to the sight by his stoutness in suffering, I continued the discipline, by intervals, till I observed him wreathing and twisting his body in a way that I could plainly perceive was not the effect of pain, but of some new and powerful sensation; curious to dive into the meaning of which, in one of my pauses of intermission, I approached, as he kept working and grinding his belly against the cushion under him; and first, stroking the untouched and unhurt side of the flesh-mount next me, then softly insinuating my hand under his thigh, felt the posture things were in forwards, which was indeed surprising; for that machine of his, which I had, by its appearance, taken for an impalpable or at best a very diminutive subject, was now, in virtue of all that smart and havock of his skin behind, grown not only to a prodigious stiffness of erection, but to a size that frighted even me: a nonpareil thickness indeed! The head of it alone filled the utmost capacity of my grasp; and when, as he heaved and wriggled it to and fro in the agitation of his strange pleasure, it came into view, it had something of the air of a round fillet of the whitest veal – like its owner, squob and short in proportion to its breadth; but when he felt my hand there, he begged I would go on briskly with my jerking, or he should never arrrive at the last stage of pleasure.

Resuming then the rod and the exercise of it, I had fairly worn out three bundles, when, after an increase of struggles and motion, and a deep sigh or two, I saw him lie still and motionless. And now he desired me

**105**

to desist, which I instantly did, and proceeding to untie him, I could not but be amazed at his passive fortitude, on viewing the skin of his butchered, mangled posteriors, late so white, smooth, and polished, now all one side of them, a confused cut-work of weals, livid flesh, gashes and gore, insomuch that when he stood up, he could scarce walk; in short, he was in sweet briars.

Then I plainly perceived on the cushion the marks of a plenteous effusion of white liquid, and already had his sluggard member run up to its old nestling-place, and ensconced itself again, as if ashamed to show its head, which nothing, it seems, could raise but stripes inflicted on its opposite neighbours, who were thus constantly obliged to suffer for his caprice . . .

He had then little to do, but to unloose the strings of my petticoat, and lift them, together with my shift, naval-high, where he just tucked them up loosely girt, and might be slipped up higher at pleasure . . .

All my back parts, naked halfway up, were now fully at his mercy: at first he stood at a convenient distance, delighting himself with a gloating survey of the attitude I lay in, and all the secret stores I thus exposed to him in fair display; then springing eagerly towards me, he covered all those naked parts with a fond confusion of kisses. And now taking hold of the rod, rather wantoned with me, in gentle inflictions on those tender trembling masses of my flesh behind, than any way hurt them, till, by degrees, he began to tingle them with smarter lashes, so as to provoke a red colour into them, which I knew, as well by the flagrant glow I felt there as by his telling me, they now emulated the native roses of my other cheeks. When he had then amused himself with admiring and toying with them, he went on to strike harder, and more hard, so that I needed all my patience not to cry out, or complain at least; at last he twigged me so smartly as to fetch blood in more than one lash, at sight of which he flung down the rod, flew to me, kissed away the starting drops, and, sucking the wounds, eased a good deal of my pain. But now raising me on my knees, and making me kneel with them straddling wide, that tender part of me, naturally the province of pleasure, not of pain, came in for its share of suffering, for now, eyeing it wistfully, he directed the rod so that the sharp ends of the twigs lighted there so sensibly that I could not help winching, and writhing my limbs with smart; so that my contortions of body must necessarily throw it into an infinite variety of postures and points of view, fit to feast the luxury of the eye. But still I bore everything without crying out: when presently, giving me another pause, he rushed, as it were, on that part whose lips and round-about had felt his cruelty, and by way of reparation, glues his own to them. Then he opened, shut and squeezed them, plucked softly the overgrowing moss, and all this in a style of wild passionate rapture and enthusiasm that expressed excess of pleasure; till betaking himself to the rod again, encouraged by my passiveness, and infuriated with this strange taste of delight, he made my poor posteriors pay for the ungovernableness of it; for now, showing them no quarter, the traitor cut me so that I wanted but very little of fainting away, when he gave over. And yet I did not utter one groan or angry expostulation; but in my heart I resolved nothing so seriously as never to expose myself again to the like severities.

You may guess then in what a curious pickle those flesh-cushions of mine were, all sore, raw, and, in fine, terribly clawed off . . . As soon as my clothes were huddled on in a little decency, a supper was brought in by the discreet Mrs Cole herself, which might have piqued the sensuality of a cardinal, accompanied with a choice of the richest wines . . .

Mrs Berkley at Charlotte Street provided the Berkley Horse, a piece of apparatus like a sloping well-padded ironing-board with rings for roping the ankles, waist and neck, and convenient apertures to admit the feet, face and erect penis. She whipped £10,000 out of this. Mrs Berkley's birches were of a dozen twigs bound together, kept in water for suppleness. She applied also the cat-o'-

nine-tails (with or without embedded needle points), straps, canes, curry-combs, battledores, holly, furze and nettles (seasonal). Her serious competitors were Mrs Jones of Hertford Street in Mayfair, Mrs Pryce of Burton Crescent and Mrs Burgess of York Square by Regent's Park, and Mrs Collett of Covent Garden (George IV was a client; whether he was an active or a passive one made speculative gossip).

Our famously flagellatory poet Algernon Swinburne was in 1868 regularly visiting a leafy villa just north of Lord's cricket ground in St John's Wood, which was luxuriously furnished and staffed by 'two golden-haired and rouge-cheeked ladies', but dreadfully expensive. Gladstone flagellated himself at home for lapsing into 'strange and humbling pursuits' with prostitutes – probably the pursuits were whippings, because he declared marital infidelity unthinkable, and he was a man of his word. The Redshawe sisters off Piccadilly offered 'ladies of refinement'; birching to its more fastidious recipients was a delicate feminine achievement comparable to whisking a soufflé. The warmly respectful affection these 'governesses' inspired was expressed by the names in print of Lady Termagant Tinglebum, Lady Bumtickler, Lady Harriet Tickletail, Lady Maria Castigate, the Countess of Greenbirch and the Duchess of Picklerod.

Of the four possible painful combinations, female flagellating male was the most common. An appreciative customer recorded in 1875:

> In my experience I have known personally several ladies of high rank who had an extraordinary passion for administering the rod, and that too with merciless severity – I knew too the wife of a clergyman, young and pretty, who carried the taste to excess – I have known only one who liked to receive it, and she was quite of the lowest order – when excited by drink she would allow herself to be birched until the bottom

was utterly raw and the rods saturated in blood, she was crying out during the operation, 'Harder, harder,' and blaspheming if it was not well laid in. At the establishment I have named in Regent's Park, there come two very young girls who go through all the phases of a schoolmistress and whip fearfully severely.

In the summer of 1863, Mrs Sarah Potter of Soho got six months for organising the birching of fourteen-year-old Agnes and seventeen-year-old Catherine, strapped naked to a ladder in an apartment called 'the schoolroom' by gentlemen with the pseudonyms 'Sealskin' and 'the Count', who tipped them a sovereign a session. At Mrs Jenkins' place, the girls were first made to sit demurely 'in class' before being stripped and flogged.

This schoolmistressy tradition of flogging had been fetchingly illustrated by James Gillray in 1786, in his etching of a plump beauty with an ostrich-feathered *coiffure*, unbuttoned to her petticoats, nipples on view, relaxed cross-thighed in an armchair, wearing an expression of delightfully fearsome anticipation, birch in hand. Her pretty lady's maid is unbuttoning the trousers of a quaking twelve-year-old. A meal and wine lie finished on the table. The title: *Lady Termagant Flaybum going to give her Stepson a taste of her Desert after Dinner.* Cost, 7s 6d.

### An English Education

Tall, strong, clergyman's widow Mrs Smith was a Gloucestershire schoolmistress, an expert on disciplining naughty girls (up to the age of twenty). Advertisements in *The Times* provided her with a domiciliary practice across the country. She wore a religious-looking gown and a Good Shepherd medallion, and performed with three-and-a-half-foot birch rods, 8d each, as advertised for sale in the *Church Times*. 'Never birch when angry,' she advised: she was a painstaking technician. The patient, wearing only her dressing-gown backwards, was strapped by ankles, wrists and waist to a narrow table, though provided with cushions underneath.

> Unfastening the dressing-gown, the orthodox surface is found at the right angle for punishing. Taking the birch, I measure my distance, and, standing at the side, proceed to strike slowly but firmly. By moving gently forward, each stroke is differently placed, and six strokes may be enough if well given *with full force*. If the fault has been such as to need severe correction, then I begin on the other side and work back again. For screams, increased strokes must be given.

It was all in Liberal MP 'Labby' Labouchère's libel-prone weekly *Truth* of 1889. Mrs Smith charged two and a half guineas a beating, and the parents could come in and enjoy it. The Dean of Lincoln was later confused to discover that he had given power to her elbow with a reference.

The attraction of preceptorial punishment was illustrated in an 1873 story, from England's bountiful flagellant fiction, about a fifteen-year-old boy and his 22-year-old delicious governess.

Demanding, 'Unfasten your braces, and pull down your trousers,' she placed him across her knees while pulling up her silk dress (to prevent it becoming creased), in which position he inhaled her perfume of violets and vervain and felt 'her soft and delicate fingers drawing up my shirt, and passing over my bare posteriors, while the warmth of her palpy forms beneath me penetrated my flesh, nature exerted her power, and my prick began to swell out to a most painful extent'. The unmerciful rod made him roar and wriggle so violently he disordered her petticoats, 'so as to expose to my delighted eyes her beautifully formed silk-clad legs up to the knees, and even an inch or two of naked thighs above'. The lad's punishment ended 'with my cheeks streaming with tears, my shirt was jutting out considerably in front in an unmistakable and most prominent manner, and my prick was at the same time throbbing beneath it with convulsive jerks'. The governess blushed, and left the room.

Further education continued the tradition less agreeably. Eton had its flagellant vocabulary. The 'flogging blocks', as much everyday necessities as Latin primers, were a couple of transportable wooden steps on which the boy ordered to 'Go down' knelt with naked buttocks, two 'holders-down' gripping his shirt, while he was flogged with a two-foot bunch of birch twigs lashed to a three-foot handle. These were prepared fresh daily by the Head Master's servant, a dozen ready each morning, and emergency supplies handy if the traffic of swishing became too heavy. Half a guinea for birches was charged on every boy's termly bill, whether he had the use of them or not.

The whole school came to watch Lower School 'executions' in the roomy schoolroom; the Upper School was birched in the 'Library', the Head Master's room, where there was always an eager crush. The 'bill' was the formal flogging list, most famously and expeditiously discharged by the Rev Dr John Keate, Head Master from 1809 to 1834, who was five foot tall, with thick, red shaggy eyebrows which he could use for pointing out things. He quacked like an angry duck and 'had such a complete command over his temper – I mean over his good temper – that he scarcely ever allowed it to appear; you could not put him out of humour – that is, out of the ill humour which he thought to be befitting for a head master', remembered historian Alexander Kinglake.

Once, a list of confirmation candidates having been

mistakenly inscribed on a 'bill', Keate flogged them all instead. It possibly made a better lesson in the unavoidability of Divine judgment. One evening Keate, excusing himself between courses from a dinner party, flogged eighty mutinous boys in a row. 'I have no remembrance of ever having seen your face before,' he confessed to an old boy in an old story. Reply: 'You were better acquainted, sir, with my other end.' Swinburne was an Old Etonian, as was Gladstone.

At Westminster, they inflicted on unruly boys four parallel apple twigs on a two-and-a-half-foot handle. At Rugby, a boy once revealed upon his buttocks the painted likeness of his master, who laughed so much he let him off. In the Navy, the boy defaulter was secured with canvas over the breech of a gun; after twelve strokes a fresh flogger then continued with a fresh birch, but the boy was given a drink of water in between. At Christ's Hospital, Charles Lamb was hauled from bed on freezing winter nights to be flogged with a leather strap if there had been any talking heard in the dorm. Milton was caned when up at Cambridge, according to Johnson.

Advertisement:

> EDUCATION
> At Mr Wackford Squeer's Academy, Dotheboys Hall,
> in the delightful village of Dotheboys, near Greta
> Bridge in Yorkshire, Youth are boarded, clothed,
> booked, furnished with pocket-money, provided with
> all necessaries, instructed in all languages living and
> dead . . . Terms, twenty guineas per annum. No extras,
> no vacations, and diet unparalleled.

One-eyed Mr Squeers whacks on.

Le vice remains as traditionally English as dreary Sundays. 'Spare the rod and spoil the child' had already been adapted from Biblical Proverbs into an English one by AD 1000. 'Six of the best' is a phrase uttered unthinkingly in English conversation. In 1972, a BBC TV comedy series about a school was readily titled 'Whack-O!' 'Bring back the birch!' remains the lusty cry of the do-good dimwits. Magistrates acquit parents accused of bruising their children's behinds. Miss Whiplash stars in the ever-running theatre of sexual fantasy, bookings from many a London telephone-box.

There are some curious delicate threads in these generously lavished thongs.

> The lion dying thrusteth forth his paw,
> And wounds the earth, if nothing else, with rage
> To be o'erpowered; and wilt thou, pupil-like
> Take thy correction mildly, kiss the rod,

the Queen mocks Richard II. She is indicating a familiar necessity of victims to kiss their instrument of torture and to ask for, and to thank for, 'an excellent whipping'. The lowering of Victorian trousers and knickers, the raising of skirts and shirts, added ceremonious relish. The obligatory exposed cleaved buttocks have been equated psychologically with the cleaved breasts, to which the hungrily feeding infant feels powerfully aggressive (thus rightly are tits and bums the fleshy foundations of England's popular newspapers). The reddening and bleeding which fascinated Fanny Hill were luscious accompaniments:

> Petticoats, etc., are then removed, and after a few
> words of lecture, during which the snowy
> prominences lie quivering in sad suspense, she
> applies the rod with such vigour and dexterity to poor
> Betty's backside, that in less than a couple of minutes
> her bouncing bum is 'all one red',

went a letter to the Editor in *Bon Ton Magazine* in 1796.

It is pleasant to think that all those involved are enjoying themselves.

**113**

**Erogenous Zones**

Voltaire scolded in his *Dictionnaire philosophique* of 1764: 'It is shameful and abominable to inflict such chastisement on *les fesses* of boys and girls.' He added: 'The two nerves which run from the anal sphincter to the pubis are stimulated, causing orgasms; it often happens to little girls.'

This neurological circle is the wedding-ring of the bottom-beating sexual relationship.

*Anatomy* The flagellatory region is served by the sacral plexus, a complicated crossover of nerves leaving the lower end of the spinal cord and mingling on the back of the pelvic basin. Emerging from this plexus, the same branches innervate the skin of the gluteal region (the bum), and the skin of the scrotum or of the female labium majus. And from the sacral plexus springs the pudendal nerve ('the nerve of shame'), which is distributed to the anus, the scrotum or the labia, and the penis or the clitoris. The onslaught of violent stimulus upon the area ruled by the sacral plexus has a spreading effect, as the gale which fills the sails stirs the sea.

The sexual stimulation of beating fellow humans was starkly depicted in the early fifteenth century by the Catalan Luis Borrassá's painting of the most potently psychological flagellation of all, that of Jesus. Two trouserless, lusty-looking floggers deploy two-handed, and held tight against their groins, whips with handles resembling erect penises with attached scrotums, the implements' three streaming white thongs matching forceful seminal emissions. The picture is an oddity worth visiting in the Musée Goya at Castres near Toulouse; though perhaps it is just a pun, *verge* being the French for both rod and penis.

That flagellation triggers erection was first observed in

114

1629 by German Dr Johann Meibom (whose anatomist
son lives on in surgery today, as a meibomian cyst of the
eyelid):

> There are persons who are stimulated to venery by
> strokes of rods, and worked up into a flame of lust by
> blows; and that the part, which distinguished us to be
> men, should be raised by the charm of invigorating
> lashes.

*Psychology*   Take-off from the concrete runways of neu-
rology into the skies of psychology was made by Freud
in 1919 with *A Child is being Beaten*, which begins:

> It is surprising how often people who seek analytic
> treatment for hysteria or an obsessional neurosis
> confess to having indulged in the phantasy: 'A child is
> being beaten' . . . The phantasy has feelings of
> pleasure attached to it . . . At the climax of the
> imaginary situation there is almost invariably a
> masturbatory satisfaction – carried out, that is to say,
> on the genitals.

The fantasy starts in early childhood, between the ages
of two and five, to be reinforced by watching children
being beaten at school. The first vision for little girls is:

> '*I am being beaten by my father.*' It is of an
> unmistakably masochistic character . . .

Later, the person beating 'turns in a characteristic way
into a representative of the father, such as a teacher'.
The little boy's fantasy is:

> . . . of being beaten by his mother for the purpose of
> masturbation, though to be sure he soon substituted
> for his own mother the mother of his school-fellows or
> other women who in some way resembled her.

**115**

It is all mixed up with the Oedipus complex:

> With boys the wish to beget a child from their mother
> is never absent, with girls the wish to have a child by
> their father is equally constant . . .

The fantasy shifts to another child being beaten –
perhaps a brother or sister – which is reversible, creating
psychological complications:

> The phantasy of the period of incestuous love had
> said: 'He (my father) loves only me, and not the other
> child, for he is beating it.' The sense of guilt can
> discover no punishment more severe than the reversal
> of this triumph: 'No, he does not love you, for he is
> beating you.' In this way the phantasy of the second
> phase, that of being beaten by her father, is a direct
> expression of the girl's sense of guilt, to which her
> love for her father has now succumbed. The phantasy,
> therefore, has become masochistic. So far as I know,
> this is always so; a sense of guilt is invariably the
> factor that transforms sadism into masochism.

Women do not much like sadistically beating maso-
chistic men (for free), but can be partial to being beaten
by them: this reflects the every-night sexual traffic, when
the male aggressively inserts, the female submissively
accepts. Though a sensible English psychological textbook sniffs:

> For the psychoanalyst, sadism has come to mean any
> attitude or activity with an element of aggression,
> masochism any tendency towards submission or the
> voluntary acceptance of an experience with a quality
> of 'un-pleasure'. It is only because of the baseless
> Freudian doctrine that the springs of all activity are to
> be found in sexuality that these words could be so
> misused. The *aggressiveness of the male* and the
> greater *dependence of the female* are more likely to
> have their origin in the necessary conditions for the

organisation of mammalian family life and in
evolutionary processes which have brought us through
tribal societies to the structure of society today, than,
as is commonly supposed, in the mere position and
mutual relation of the male and female in the act of
coitus.

Twenty-four years separate the lives of a French noble-
man who survived the Revolution and died in 1824 and
an Austrian police chief's son who wrote successfully of
small-town life in the eastern reaches of the Hapsburg
Empire, and later *Venus in Furs*, and who died in 1895
in western Prussia. Had they met for dinner overlooking
the Rhine, the Marquis de Sade and Leopold von Sacher-
Masoch would have fitted together wonderfully.

This weird human frailty of the equally enjoyable
infliction and receipt of pain, that taxed the most learned
psychological treatment, was cured on 11 March 1993 by
the British House of Lords. Its judges refused freedom to
five men appealing against their conviction for beating,
wounding, branding, and bleeding each other, and for
'genital torture including the use of sandpaper, fish-
hooks, scalpels and hot wax', as well as for 'violence to
the buttocks, anus, penis, testicles and nipples.'

'If it was to be decided that such activities as the
nailing by A of B's foreskin or scrotum to a board, or the
insertion of hot wax into C's urethra followed by the
burning of his penis with a candle, or the incising of D's
scrotum with a scalpel, or the effusion of blood, were
injurious to neither B, C and D, nor to the public interest,
it was for Parliament with its accumulated wisdom and
sources of information to declare them lawful,' declared
the Lords Justices of this admittedly somewhat overdoing
it with *le vice anglais*. They perceived: 'There was no
evidence to support the assertion that sadomasochistic
activities were essential to the happiness of the
appellants.'

117

So much for Freud. But he was not even English, though privileged to die in Hampstead.

The House of Lords similarly decided on 18 October 1990, when passing the Human Fertilization and Embryology Bill, to disregard the Divine activity recorded in Genesis and recreate human life, which was to start at twenty-four weeks after successful copulation. England may suffer a laughable vice, but splendidly enjoys single-minded and uncompromising lawgivers, because they, like God, are unelected.

## Muggletonians and Others

Lodowicke Muggleton was born in 1609 in Walnut Tree Yard off Bishopsgate in London, the son of a farrier, and was apprenticed to a tailor who specialised in City livery. In 1625, he recovered from the plague and afterwards never 'spent sixpence on physic' all his life. In 1630, he became both engaged and a pawnbroker, until his fiercely puritan cousin John Reeve put a stop to both youthful ventures. Lodowicke was tall and handsome, sharp-nosed, full-lipped, with auburn hair flowing to his shoulders, a zealous puritan in white neckbands, but who 'enjoyed his pipe and glass'. It became clear to him at the age of forty-two, and now twice a widower, that he and his cousin were mentioned in the Book of Revelation, chapter 11:

> And I will give power unto my two witnesses, and they shall prophesy a thousand two hundred and threescore days, clothed in sackcloth. These are the two olive trees, and the two candlesticks standing before the God of the earth. And if any man will hurt them, fire proceedeth out of their mouth, and devoureth their enemies: and if any man will hurt them, he must in this manner be killed.

Their powers so bestowed extended to turning water into blood, smiting the earth with plagues and stopping it raining. A year later, on 3 February 1652, John Reeve announced that Jesus had confirmed all this to him in person.

Lodowicke Muggleton became 'The Prophet of Walnut Tree Yard', and his disciples were embellished with worthy City merchants. The Muggletonians believed that God had a human body, had left Elijah as His locum in Heaven when He was on earth as Jesus, and that after His revelation to Lodowicke and his cousin He no longer saw any need to meddle with the machinery of the world. Muggletonians condemned prayer and preaching, thought faith divine and reason the creation of the Devil; witchcraft was a delusion, the miracles were parables, the sun moved round the earth and heaven was six miles away.

Lodowicke was twice imprisoned in Bridewell for blasphemy, and also got three days in the pillory, his books being burned before his face. Sickly John Reeve died six years after meeting Jesus, but Lodowicke reached the age of eighty-nine and the Muggletonian sect lived on until 1846. There were still enough of them to reprint their founder's views in his *Divine Looking-Glass* of 1656, and to perpetuate in theology so snug a name.

The number of religious cults is as limitless as the unusual – or eccentric, or lunatic – ideas which can entice believers and glorify their leaders. Freud romantically explained such wildly uncritical idealisation as a mass falling in love. The past quarter-century has produced a fashionable outbreak of such passions. Fifteen thousand new religions have arisen in Britain, their membership varying from 100,000 to twenty-five, their beliefs ranging from 'no premarital sex' to 'living for ever'. In the USA they are countless, and reach regularly to Britain for eager recruits.

119

In November 1978, 913 followers of the Rev Jim Jones killed themselves, all together, with cyanide-laced fruit juice in the Guyana jungle. In April 1993, eighty-six followers of David Koresh's Branch Davidian cult burnt themselves alive in Texas. An attractive idea binds powerfully, unto the death.

In the *Westminster Gazette* of 25 February 1905:

> It is reported that a society has been founded in Leeds the object of which is to persuade all and sundry that the world is flat, and not, as so many of us ignorantly suppose, round . . . it will be interesting to see how it thrives in the shrewd Yorkshire air.

The society thrives still in the credulous air of California. Founded in 1800, its 2,000 members, shadowing the Muggletonians, admirably scorn theory in the face of evidence. They see the spinning-ball notion as absurd. The earth is not a planet but infinite in size, the land and water were shaken apart by God, and the Australians do not hang by their feet like sloths.

If you want fervently to embrace a freakish idea join the Flat Earth Society, which has not killed anyone yet, even from falling off the edge.

# NINE

# Blunting the Edge

At the start of this century, Freud had defined our instinctive avoidance of anything hurtful as 'the pleasure principle'. By 1920, he had advanced to *Beyond the Pleasure Principle*. This was a monograph about humanity's unconscious instinct for self-destruction – the death wish, 'thanatos' (the Greek word was never used by Freud, but was applied by the Viennese physician Wilhelm Stekel, whom he hated). Freud perceived through the periscope of our mental submarine:

> We have unwittingly steered our course into the harbour of Schopenhauer's philosophy. For him death is the 'true result and to that extent the purpose of life', while the sexual instinct is the embodiment of the will to live.

The love instinct is the drive towards the preservation of ourselves and our species. The death instinct is the drive towards extinction, expressed by suicide, drink and drugs, smoking, unhealthiness, recklessness, accidents, fights and wars. They may combine: what a pleasant unification of the first necessity with the second peril is overeating a deliciously cooked meal.

## The Flowing Bowl

$C_2H_5OH$ – ethanol, or ethyl alcohol – is a simple compound which boils at 78.3°C, freezes at −114.5°C, and has a density at 40°C of 0.772. It burns with the considerable heat of 7.11 kcal/gm to evolve $H_2O$ and $CO_2$, and its vapour forms an explosive mixture with air. Ethanol is a popular solvent for many organic compounds and mineral salts, particularly those insoluble in water (e.g., iodine, perfumes, soap), and it readily dissolves most gases (e.g., per 100 volumes at atmospheric pressure, 7 of H, or 30 of $CO_2$). Its strong affinity for water makes ethanol a convenient drying agent, and it is difficult to prepare in pure anhydrous form. Ethanol is manufactured mostly from $C_2H_4$ – ethylene – which is produced by oil refineries, but it can be synthesised also by the action of yeast on glucose (e.g., as found respectively upon the skins, and in the juice, of grapes).

A dose of ethanol administered orally to humans is absorbed rapidly from the lining of the mouth, gullet and stomach, but 80 per cent of it is ingested from the small intestine which coils in the abdomen beyond them. Within five minutes, ethanol becomes detectable chemically in the circulating blood. Ethanol distributes itself throughout the entire body, its concentration in the cerebrospinal fluid surrounding the brain, and in the urine, becoming higher than in the blood. Five per cent of the dose is excreted unchanged in the urine, the breath and the sweat, and 95 per cent is metabolised by the liver. The hepatic enzyme cytoplasmic alcohol dehydrogenase changes ethanol into acetaldehyde ($C_2H_4O$), which the enzyme acetaldehyde dehydrogenase then converts to acetylcoenzyme A, which enters the Krebs' tricarboxylic acid cycle to become finally carbon dioxide and water. The chemical ethanol provokes the oldest, and the most widespread, persistent, incurable, fascinating, frustrating, agitating, taxing (and taxed) of all human frailties.

After a miserable, rainy voyage, with a difficult, noisy cargo, lasting seven months and seventeen days until the Ark bumped down at Ararat, what did Noah do?

> And Noah began to be an husbandman, and he planted a vineyard: and he drank of the wine, and was drunken; and he was uncovered within his tent.

Alexander Cruden ventured further towards the Creation in his *Biblical Concordance* of 1737:

> Several of the ancients were of opinion, that wine was not in use before the deluge, and that Noah was the first who used this liquor. If wine, they say, had been known before the flood, Abel would not have failed to bring an offering of it to the Lord, and Noah would have been on his guard, so as not to have drank of it to excess. But, on the other hand, it is maintained by others, that it is much more probable that the first men were not ignorant of the use of wine, which is a liquor so generally useful and agreeable, that it could scarcely be unknown even to Adam himself. And as to Noah, they say, that though he knew the intoxicating quality of wine, yet he might be deceived in the strength of it, and think, that the quantity he drank of it was not capable of causing the drunkenness in him that he afterwards found it did.

Alexander Cruden continued by anticipating the poncy wine critics of the Sunday papers:

> There were many excellent vineyards in Palestine. The wine of Helbron: Ezekiel speaks of this wine that was sold at the fairs of Tyre. Some say that this wine was well known to the ancients; they called it *Chalibonium vinum*. It was made at Damascus, and the Persians had planted vineyards there, on purpose, as Posidonius affirms. Others make it a common name, sweet or fat wine; for Helbron comes from a word that

123

signifies fat. The wine of Lebanon: Hosea speaks of this wine 'The scent thereof shall be as the wine of Lebanon.' The wines of those sides of mount Lebanon that had a good exposition to the sun, were therefore much esteemed. But some think, that the Hebrew text 'wine of Lebanon' may signify a sweet-scented wine; wine in which perfumes are mixed, or other drugs, to make it more palatable, and of a better flavour. Odoriferous wines were not unknown to the Hebrews. In the Song of Solomon mention is made of a medicated wine, spiced wine, wine mixed with perfumes. The wines of Palestine being heady, they used to qualify them with water, that they might be drunk without any inconvenience.

There is plenty of wine about in Genesis. Jacob's son Judah 'washed his garments in wine, and his clothes in the blood of grapes: his eyes shall be red with wine'. Even if the grape did not precede the cider-apple in the Garden of Eden, mankind has been dosing himself with ethanol longer than his recorded memory. The reason is a simple pharmacological action: ethanol depresses that part of the central nervous system which elevates him above the beasts.

'Drink thy wine with a merry heart,' encourages Ecclesiastes. The merriment reflects that man's higher mental centres, which discipline behaviour, become inhibited first. Unfortunately, such lack of self-control extends to the rash repetition of doses. This results in a traditional progression:

| Mg ethanol/ 100 ml blood | State |
| --- | --- |
| Nil | Dry and decent |
| 80 | Drunken driver |
| 100 | Delighted and devilish |
| 200 | Dizzy and delirious |
| 300 | Dazed and dejected |
| 400 | Dead drunk |
| 500 | Dead |

This template of behaviour has stamped mankind with most of its misfortunes – according to enthusiastic groups who wish to return self-dosage with ethanol to a non-existence it suffered only before verse one of Genesis.

It is a human frailty to drink. But prohibitionists suffer another human frailty: of self-importance achieved through good causes. Good causes vary in their value. To their opponents – such as an antagonistic nation at war – they can be horribly bad causes. Whether the do-gooders' campaigning, or its objective, is worth all the fuss is a particular they overlook in the fervour that binds them together like the enthusiasts of any other cult. We have seen that when everyone you mingle with thinks that something is true, then it must be, and if it is righteous as well you feel lovely.

Civilisation's magnificent achievement in 1920, of converting a vast, orderly, rich, educated and admired nation to alcoholic abstinence, a transfiguration comparable in history to the enlightening of the world's savages with Christianity, disintegrated rapidly into a squalid and murderous shambles.

Prohibition lay in the early, uncontaminated American soul like puritanism. By the middle of the nineteenth century, temperance societies were flourishing in New England with the vigour of the Salem witch-hunters 150 years earlier. Massachusetts in 1838 essayed sobriety by prohibiting the sale of 'less than 15 gallons of spirituous liquor . . . at one time', but in 1840 this was repealed as a bad idea. In 1851 Maine went dry, and New York State followed on 4 July 1855, the Mayor of New York genially instructing his enforcing police to exercise 'great circumspection, and be careful to avoid seizing' any possibly intoxicating liquors. Indiana and Georgia were puddled wet and dry. Thirteen states entered into aridity, but through the agitation of their drinkers they were mostly remoistened by their own supreme courts.

After the Civil War of 1861–65, the nineteenth-century impulse that America somehow needed reform grew stronger and better organised. Moral uplift is useless without lobbyists. When the teetotallers gesticulating piously from Plymouth Rock felt the rising tide of liquor entering their boots, they were stimulated to amalgamate and act as prudently as any other powerful, self-interested political group.

The National Prohibition Party was founded in Chicago in 1869, and the Women's Christian Temperance Union at Cleveland in 1874 – the climacteric of women against liquor in the Middle West (Mrs Annie Wittenmyer, first president). Ohio reinforced these crusaders in 1893 with the Anti-Saloon League, which was to become the most effective national prohibition lobby, and to offer glittering renown to its leaders.

Wayne B. Wheeler was born of a New England family on an Ohio farm in 1869, and worked his way through the local Oberlin college as a janitor and part-time chaplain. He was a keen student speaker, who 'poured out his soul in youthful ardour, anathematising the saloon and predicting its final overthrow' (he had been scared by drunks as a child). Many careers have been ruined by drink; Wayne B. Wheeler's was founded on it. In 1893 he became manager of the Ohio Anti-Saloon League, later the Anti-Saloon League of America, immediately diverting himself into law school to develop extra muscle.

Wayne B. Wheeler was impatient with fiddly education to reduce national drinking, though the Women's Christian Temperance Union had perseveringly achieved compulsory anti-alcohol lessons in all American public schools. 'We'll make them believe in punishment after death,' was his more vigorous approach. He had 'a passionate sincerity that bordered unscrupulousness', and later an enthusiasm for extreme measures in enforcing the prohibition laws, including calling out the Army

126

and US Navy (which remains high and dry, following his pilotage in 1914). This professional prohibitionist was the antithesis of the oft-imprisoned Mrs Carry Nation of Kansas, who in the 1890s unsubtly led hymn-singing women with hatchets into saloons to smash them up and then smash up their liquor stocks.

Wayne B. Wheeler was insignificant-looking, balding, stubble-moustached, a Republican. His spectacular front man was a bulky, loquacious, Bible-trumpeting pacifist, the thrice-failed Democratic Presidential candidate William Jennings Bryan, secretly paid by the Anti-Saloon League $11,000 a year. The Anti-Saloon League had become rich. Its fund-raisers lived on commission from their collections (up to 20 per cent for the first $25,000, 30 per cent thereafter, big money when accepting regular expressions of John D. Rockefeller Jr's high-mindedness). In March 1914, Wayne B. Wheeler won the Anti-Saloon League a national victory by pushing through Congress, and over Republican President Taft's veto, the Webb-Kenyon Act to forbid liquor entering states where it was illegal to sell it. The Act stimulated Arizona, Colorado and Virginia to lead individual states once more into prohibition, and it stimulated the prohibitionists to spread their tarpaulin coast-to-coast.

Worthy citizens complacently concurred to redirecting their straying fellows on to the paths of abstinent righteousness, towards family-loving constancy and to decorous behaviour. Employers rubbed their hands at getting more work out of sober workers for their wages. The southern states overtook the New Englanders in prohibitory zeal, because it would stop the blacks becoming inflamed sexually towards white women. In the rousing religious procession, the Presbyterians led the Protestants and then the grudging Catholics, who seldom found sinful dregs in their wine. The politicians of both parties exchanged sanctimoniousness for votes, and ended in an alcoholic heap. Everyone in America forgot that when the huddled masses got off at Ellis Island, the first thing they wanted, like Noah, was a drink.

A prohibition amendment to the Constitution had been first suggested in 1846, by John Bartholomew Gogh, a reformed drunk. Twenty years later, it reached the floor of the House through the representative of New Hampshire. The famous Eighteenth Amendment of 1917, monumentalising prohibition, was passed by the Senate by 65 to 20 votes in August, and with minor modifications adopted by the House of Representatives the week before Christmas. The Amendment was briskly ratified by the states, the necessary 36th voting on 29 January 1919. It had taken only thirteen months, and was proudly claimed by Wayne B. Wheeler as prompt enlightenment from his evangelism.

Two-thirds of the states had already become dry by their own laws when the Volstead Act enforcing the Eighteenth Amendment fell upon America on 16 January 1920. The Act was the Anti-Saloon League's clamorously yearned-for triumph. It was conducted through the Senate by the next US President, Warren Harding, from Wayne B. Wheeler's home state. The Act was then vetoed by Democratic President Woodrow Wilson on 27 October 1919, and repassed by Congress the next day.

Wilson was unpopular for getting the US into the Great War, for his 'fourteen points' structuring its peace, for entangling himself with the wily Europeans, and for championing the League of Nations. The Senate, which on 19 March 1920 preferred national isolation to dutifully ratifying the Treaty of Versailles and voted against it, felt that President Wilson should have his nose further rubbed into indignity. Thus great issues are influenced by irrelevant reasons, for both rulers and voters, underlining the unreliability of party politics and referendums.

William Jennings Bryan passionately welcomed prohi-

128

bition to the wintry Washington midnight chimes, predicting that its blessing would rapidly spread to Europe and beyond, as foreign befuddled nations found themselves unable to compete with a sober America. An hour later that night in Chicago, an armed masked gang stole $100,000 worth of whisky off the railroad. Thus was plainly inaugurated an experiment for which the befuddled nations must be perpetually grateful to America for the value of its failure.

As the Volstead Act was the Anti-Saloon League's *raison d'être*, the League might have comfortably anticipated itself disappearing, as Engels expected the State to wither away in the heaven of Communism. But the US Government was now enthusiastically assisted by the population in its discovery of the difficulties of administering the new law. As alcohol enjoyed a medical aroma, it could be prescribed by your doctor – in doses up to half a pint every ten days. He was allowed for this popular therapy a hundred prescriptions every ninety days.

The United States had overnight become awash with impounded liquor, which could not be passed to the public but could be sold to other warehouses. A Chicago lawyer, George Remus, bought the stored booze and distributed it through his pharmaceutical companies as medicine, allowing himself an amplitude of commercial discretion that ended him in jail. The Governor of New York meanwhile tried serving up light wines and 2.75%-alcohol beer, but the US Supreme Court disagreed and stopped the party.

Quebec was a dripping *robinet* into the Eastern US states, off whose stormy seaboard the Rum Row armada hove-to outside territorial waters, in defiance of both the US Customs and some unsportsmanlike pirating fellow-bootleggers. Fast motorboats became the New York tipplers' lifeboats, dodging the Coastguard cutters to the

**129**

shore. The fleet's John Paul Jones was Captain Bill McCoy of the British-registered *Tomoka*, whose cargo from Nassau was of such reliability – unlike Havana rum or Mexican rye – that he achieved the eponym 'The Real McCoy'. (Possibly: prizefighter Kid McCoy had thus earlier fought off his imitators, and McCoy was already a good whisky in 1908.)

Locking up every speakeasy was remotely beyond the overstretched and unenthusiastic prohibition agents, who were on an invitingly bribable $40 a week. Only the fat and feared Izzy Einstein and Moe Smith achieved effectiveness and national fame, through Holmesian disguises and a rubber tube from the top pocket to the underarm flask of evidence.

The chief prohibition prosecutor, energetic, morning cold-bather Assistant Attorney General Mrs Mabel Willebrandt, became so exasperated that she abided the dry Ku Klux Klan – 'I have no objections to people dressing up in sheets if they enjoy that sort of thing' – and retired in 1928 to advise the Californian makers of Vine-Glo, a grape concentrate sold with the warning that, with the addition of sugar and water, it had the danger in sixty days of producing 12 per cent alcohol. In Chicago, Al 'Scarface' Capone and the rival bootlegging gangs were shooting their way into American history. 'Our trouble lies in the lax conscience of a very considerable proportion of our citizens,' perceived President Harding.

Prohibition had changed, not eradicated, American drinking habits. President and Mrs Harding entertained with highballs in their White House bedroom. The influence of Wayne B. Wheeler was watered down, as he was increasingly suspected only to have made the country drink more. The League against saloons had simply spawned three times the number of speakeasies, and the legal, and far greater illegal, finances had deepened the Depression.

Employers were now subsidising the repealers, having discovered that sober workers were worse than drunk ones. Over 4,000 drinkers a year were dying from poisonous methyl alcohol, the corpses by 1927 being laid at Wayne B. Wheeler's door. His wife was burnt to death that summer by an exploding stove, while her horrified father instantaneously slumped dead from a heart attack, and within a month Wayne B. Wheeler himself was dead from nephritis, aged fifty-eight.

At Chicago in 1929, the Women's Organisation for National Prohibition Reform was founded by Mrs Annie Wittenmyer's historical opposite, redheaded Mrs Pauline Sabin. In 1932, John D. Rockefeller Jr withdrew his generosity from the Anti-Saloon League, and New York Governor Franklin D. Roosevelt pronounced the futility of the Eighteenth Amendment, then was elected President. The Twenty-first Amendment scotched the Eighteenth at three in the afternoon of 5 December 1933, when Utah completed the three-quarters of states needed to approve. It was the only US Constitutional amendment ever to be repealed. 'Wine, which cheereth God and man', flowed in America as it had in the Bible. It is splendid to legislate against a sin, but first you must be sure that it is one.

Britain had not prohibition but the Permissive Bill, not the Anti-Saloon League but the United Kingdom Alliance. This was inaugurated in 1853 for the 'Total and Immediate Legal Suppression of the Traffic in all intoxicating Liquors'. It was inspired in Manchester by the state sobriety of Maine. By 1856, the Alliance had 30,000 members paying a shilling each, and 500 meetings swelled by approving outsiders from the multitude who aspired to the Victorian ideal of respectability.

The Alliance was predominantly Nonconformist, Liberal and northern. The Lancashire textile manufacturers, like the American bosses, anticipated more work from sober workers for their money and, better still, higher profits from their employees buying new shirts instead of drink. Trade unionists were equally enthusiastic, perceiving that the workers could better stand up to the unscrupulous employers when not stupefied by drink. The Alliance attracted the future Cardinal Manning, and Lord Brougham the law reformer, of the one-horse closed carriage, who discovered Cannes. But John Stuart Mill scowlingly recognised the Alliance only as an intolerable and dangerous encroachment upon individual liberty.

A sporting landowner, Sir Wilfrid Lawson, MP for Carlisle, bemusedly found himself the Alliance's Parliamentary voice, and dutifully continued uttering for forty years his support for the Permissive Bill. This would have given a two-thirds majority of local ratepayers the power to shut the pubs. When he introduced the Bill into the House of Commons in 1864, it was defeated by a majority of 257. With growing national uneasiness about drunkenness, and a readiness for reform of the licensing laws, the sneerers in Parliament fell in 1869 to 106, and in 1870 to 31. But the publicans were powerful, the brewers were munificent friends of the Tories, and Mr Gladstone could justifiably complain after losing to Disraeli in 1874 that he had been 'borne down in a torrent of gin and beer'. If the Permissive Bill awaited a House of Commons majority of teetotal MPs, Lawson saw gloomily they would 'wait until doomsday'. And under the universally admired British Constitution, there was always 'a good drunken majority in the House of Lords to throw it out'.

So Hogarth's Gin Lane remained open, if a one-way street with a dead end. Britain was nevertheless persistently enjoined to sobriety by the Church of England Temperance Society, the British and Foreign Temperance Society (Queen Victoria, patron) and a dozen others, which included societies for the Army and the Royal

Navy. Their urging was augmented by the International Order of Good Templars, the Band of Hope for youth, and the sounding brass and tinkling tambourines of the Salvation Army. The upshot of such energetic and earnest activity was the mild restriction of pub opening hours, with the afternoon gap of teatime abstinence, introduced by Lloyd George in 1916 to discourage the apparently incorrigibly drunken workers from deranging the munition factories of the Great War. Britain being Britain, the prohibition survived the peace and another war, until flicked away in 1985 by Mrs Thatcher's duster.

Ireland's consumption of spirits halved from 10,815,000 gallons a year between 1838 and 1842, after the temperance mission of charismatic Father Mathew from Tipperary – assisted by the potato famine, when a third of all Irishmen died from starvation or from 'famine fever', typhus. The flowing schnapps of Norway and Iceland, the vodka of Finland, the raki of Turkey, all suffered transient damming. In France, the instruction of schoolchildren in temperance became compulsory in 1902. Small, bleak notices about *l'ivresse* are pinned up in the cafés, but temperance movements there have not caught public imagination.

Human despair over remedying our frailty for reaching out for glasses of various ethanol mixtures has usefully inspired rethinking. A good cause is not good enough. The solution is no longer the strident public pursuit of universal abolition but, more intelligently and cautiously, a private and sympathetic invitation to the victims. Eighteen months after the crashing failure of prohibition, Alcoholics Anonymous was conceived in Akron, Ohio, by a New York stockbroker and a local doctor, both drunks.

'AA' is a club of people who have lost control of their drinking. All that is asked of them is the admission 'I am an alcoholic'. They must warily never claim to be cured, only to be a sober alcoholic. AA has no membership list, no files, no fees, no religion, no preaching, no advertising, no fund-raising, no snooping; it asks no names and never fusses if you want to leave. It has two million members. In Britain, two-thirds are male, a third are in their forties, a quarter come from the boss class, a tenth each are housewives, retired, and unemployed. The therapy is to meet and to tell one another what drinking did to them, and how they stopped. The prescription is to stay away from a drink, one day at a time. Forty-one per cent have remained sober for ten years, 16 per cent for longer. These are high figures, when the alternative is nil. There is no alcoholic therapist more effective than a recovered one.

Alcohol Concern – and other bodies expressing it – tilts an equally workmanlike eye at the 7.2 litres a head of 100 per cent ethanol swallowed every year by the British, who by the time they turn fifteen are, 34 per cent of boys and 28 per cent of girls, regular drinkers. The British employ over a million people to serve them the drinks for which they pay £24 billion a year. The Government responds 'Cheers!' for 5.1 per cent of its tax revenue – £8 billion – simultaneously paying out £6 million a year to instruct the population how to stop drinking, an exchange which would have created another confusion for Alice in Wonderland. The Americans down 7.8 litres a year of pure ethanol, the French 12.6, the Swiss 11.2, the Hungarians 12.2, the Australians 8.8, but the Peruvians manage only 1.4 and the Koreans 1.2.

The fearsome demon drink has changed vulnerably from a moral evil to a medical one.

The pathological effects of ethanol are:

- 1 *Nervous System*   Amnesia, insomnia, convulsions, hallucinations, Wernicke's encephalopathy (confusion and eye dysfunction), Korsakow's psychosis

**134**

(disorientation in time and space) and the Marchiafava-Bignamia syndrome (dementia, fits, paralysis).

- 2 *Alimentary system*   Gastritis, ulcers, blood-vomiting, inhaling vomit, the Mallory-Weiss syndrome (vomiting so hard you rip your gullet), cancer, hepatitis, cirrhosis of the liver, infection of the pancreas, gout.
- 3 *Metabolism*   A pint of beer contains 180 calories, a small Scotch 58, a glass of Burgundy 80, a small sherry 75. So ethanol is the slimmer's ruin, both in itself and in its uninhibiting effect towards the roast potatoes and second helpings of pudding.
- 4 *Blood*   Anaemia, susceptibility to infections.
- 5 *Obstetrics*   Foetal damage.

In 1987, the Royal College of Physicians of London proclaimed a drinker's unit to be a half-pint of beer, or a small glass of wine or a small tot of spirits. The College set a daily limit of three. This was hardly Falstaffian rations. Such advice first spread disbelief and derision, but the Royal College of Physicians knows what it is talking about. Drinking costs the British National Health Service £150 million a year and shortens life expectancy by 10 per cent.

We are growing obsessed about our health, because the tangible delights of this world now so outdo the fanciful ones of the next that everyone has become deeply concerned to stay in it as long as possible. To stop frail humans from tippling themselves into an early grave, the hypochondria of this age should be more promising than the holiness of ages past.

But sadly it will not be. Incorrigible humans will apply common sense to their drinking as meagerly, as we shall now see, as to their smoking. It is no excuse to remember:

> And all the days of Noah were nine hundred and fifty years: and he died.

**135**

TEN

# The Last Gasper

Witty, airy Charles Stuart Calverley was a Worcestershire clergyman's son orignally named Blayds, who went up to Oxford from Harrow in 1850, won the Chancellor's prize for Latin verse but was sent down for larking about. He migrated to Cambridge and became a fellow of Christ's College. *The Cambridge History of English Literature* compliments this as 'his noble apology for tobacco':

*Ode to Tobacco*

Thou who, when fears attack,
Bidst them avaunt, and Black
Care, at the horseman's back
Perching, unseatest;
Sweet, when the morn is gray;
Sweet, when they've cleared away
Lunch; and at close of day
Possibly sweetest:

I have a liking old
For thee, though manifold
Stories, I know, are told,
Not to thy credit;
How one (or two at most)
Drops make a cat a ghost –
Useless, except to roast –
Doctors have said it:

How they who use fusees
All grow by slow degrees
Brainless as chimpanzees,
Meagre as lizards;
Go mad, and beat their wives;
Plunge (after shocking lives)
Razors and carving knives
Into their gizzards.

Confound such knavish tricks!
Yet know I five or six
Smokers who freely mix
Still with their neighbours;
Jones — (who, I'm glad to say,
Asked leave of Mrs J.) —
Daily absorbs a clay
After his labours.

Cats may have had their goose
Cooked by tobacco-juice;
Still why deny its use
Thoughtfully taken?
We're not as tabbies are:
Smith, take a fresh cigar!
Jones, the tobacco jar!
Here's to thee, Bacon!

Calverley had a skating accident in 1866, suffered brain damage and remained an invalid until he died in 1884 of Bright's disease. He translated Theocritus into English verse and wrote two volumes of crystalline light poetry. He did also a poem on beer. The Bacon he saluted in 1871 is the Market Hill tobacconist where I bought my own cork-tipped Craven A and de Reskes between dissecting the dead in the Cambridge medical school.

Smoking in my medical student days was a casual human frailty. Everybody did it. A non-smoker was an oddity like a vegetarian or a nudist. Smoking was the ritual of civilisation: the tapping the butt, the flipping the petrol-lighter, the quick draw, the languid exhalation, the clever smoke-rings, the flicking the ash. How familiar were the nonchalant Noël Coward cigarette holder, the flustered Wooster gasper, the Sherlock Holmes pipe, Tommy Atkins' Woodbines, Churchill's cigars, initialled silver cigarette cases ('Virginia on the left, Turkish on the right'). Over the radio came *Smoke Gets in Your Eyes* and *A Cigarette that Bears a Lipstick's Traces*; everyone except Shirley Temple smoked wildly on stage and on screen. You puffed as unthinkingly as you drew breath, in those days before King George VI died of it.

*Nicotiana tabacum* is a native plant of South America, Mexico and the West Indies. It grows five feet tall, has broad two-foot leaves and pink flowers which open at night. The leaf is cured by laying it out in the sun or hanging it in airy barns or by the smoke of wood or charcoal. China is the largest tobacco producer, then USA, India, Brazil and the old USSR. Backward countries contain 70 per cent of the world's land that is given up to cultivating tobacco.

Christopher Columbus discovered the American Indians smoking both curatively and ceremonially – the pipe of peace was a solemn ignition. American tobacco became a European curiosity, which in 1561 Jean Nicot, the French ambassador to Lisbon, presented to his Queen, Catherine de' Medici, so making it fashionable, giving his name to it, and starting everybody sniffing snuff. In 1586, the first Governor of Virginia brought an Indian pipe home for Sir Walter Raleigh, whose endorsement through his courtly enjoyment of smoking it began spreading the popularity of pipes throughout Europe. Raleigh spent £40,000 on three expeditions to colonise America for his doting Queen Elizabeth; but the colonists all died or came home, and all he could show for her money was tobacco and potatoes.

Europeans, like the American Indians, thought smoking an agreeable way of doing themselves good. In his *English Physician* of 1653, the Spittlefields herbalist

Nicholas Culpeper listed the remedial effects of home-grown tobacco:

It is a hot martial plant. A slight infusion of the fresh
gathered leaves vomits, and that very roughly; but for
constitutions that can bear it, it is a good medicine for
rheumatic pains; an ointment made of them, with
hog's lard, is good for the piles when they get painful
and are inflamed. The distilled oil is sometimes
dropped on cotton, and applied to aching teeth, and it
seldom fails to give a temporary relief. The powdered
leaves, or a decoction of them, kill lice, and other
vermin. The smoke of tobacco injected, in the manner
of a clyster, is of singular efficacy in obstinate
stoppages of the bowels, for destroying those small
worms called ascarides, and for the recovery of
persons apparently drowned. A constant chewing, or
smoking of tobacco, hurts the appetite, by depriving
the constitution of too much saliva; but though it is
improper for lean, dry, hectic people, it may be useful
to the more gross, and to such as are subject to cold
diseases. Snuff is seldom productive of any bad
effects, unless it be swallowed, but it should not be
used by such as are inclined to an apoplexy. Tobacco
is a great expeller of phlegm when smoked in a pipe,
in which vast quantities are consumed, the greatest
part by way of amusement, though some command it
as a helper of digestion; many extol it as a preservative
from the plague; but Rivinus says, that in the plague of
Leipsic several died who were great smokers of
tobacco. The distilled oil is of a poisonous nature; a
drop of it, taken inwardly, will destroy a cat.

The Great Plague of London was an impetus to smoking
to stave off infection.

Thomas Hearne, in his Diary, writes: '1720–21,
January 2. I have been told that in the last great Plague
at London, none that kept tobacconists' shops had the
plague, it is certain that smoking was looked upon as a
most excellent preservative, insomuch that even

**139**

children were obliged to smoke. And I remember that I heard formerly Tom Rogers, who was yeoman-beadle, say, that when he was that year, when the plague raged, a school boy at Eton, all the boys of that school were obliged to smoke in the school every morning, and that he was never whipped so much in his life as he was one morning for not smoking,'

reported John Timbs in his *Doctors and Patients* of 1873.

In the June of deadly 1665, Samuel Pepys saw for the first time the foot-high red crosses and the plea 'Lord have mercy upon us' splashed on the doors of Drury Lane houses. These omens shut them up for forty days, with the plague victim and the yet uninfected family inside. The ghoulish sight 'put me into an ill conception of myself and my smell, so that I was forced to buy some roll-tobacco to smell and to chaw – which took away my apprehension'.

The soothing effect of tobacco so appreciated by Pepys became widely enjoyed through 'the sweet post-prandial cigar', the foot-and-a-half-long clay churchwarden, the painted porcelain pipe bowls of the Bavarians, the American corncob, the elaborate Persian hookah. It spread immensely after the perils of the Crimean War were conveniently dulled through the combatants' discovery of the handy Turkish cigarette.

The Spanish *cigarito*, which reached Europe early in the sixteenth century, was first rolled by the Aztecs, using cornhusks. It had attained the elegance of the London drawing-room by 1891: 'A cigarette is the perfect type of a perfect pleasure. It is exquisite, and it leaves one unsatisfied. What more can one want?' suggested Oscar Wilde. After steeling the world through two other wars, 36 billion cigarettes were smoked in Britain in 1920 and 113 billion in 1961. The United States similarly smoked 18 billion in 1915, 124 billion in 1930 and 400 billion in 1950.

The cat liable to instant death through ingesting a drop of tobacco-juice is a portentous spectre which leaps two hundred years from Culpeper and Calverley. Everyone living earlier in this smoky twentieth century felt vaguely that the habit was somehow 'bad for you'. Children were warned that smoking would stunt their growth, women sighed that it stained brown their manicured fingers, the sufferers from 'smoker's cough' shrugged off their disease like flat feet. The votaries of the ashtray felt the same carping, but unhampering, wickedness as those of the glass. During an awkward moment of the blitz, I found myself sharing a doorway near my hospital with a tart, to whom I offered a sustaining cigarette. 'Oh, thank you!' she said, gratefully and guiltily, taking one. 'My only vice.'

'Yet the captain of all these men of death that had come against him to take him away, was the consumption, for it was that that brought him down to the grave,' observed Mr Wiseman about Mr Badman in 1680. Consumption has been demoted. Today there marches upon us more fearsomely the duo of Captain Coronary, who with his artery-attacking lieutenants slaughters some 300,000 Britons and a million Americans a year, and Captain Cancer, who annually massacres 163,000 Britons and half a million Americans. A quarter of his enemies are shot neatly through the lungs.

In the middle of this century the cancerous sniper's weapon was identified: tobacco smoke. An easy victory in the world's everlasting war against disease was in sight, to spare the lives of 40,000 British and 125,000 Americans hit by lung cancer between one Christmas and the next, and uncountable lives elsewhere. People would simply stop smoking. This was a medical advance as significant as Pasteur's discovery of microbes in 1864, of Lister's surgical antisepsis of 1865, of Florey's injecting penicillin in 1940, of Jenner's conception of vaccination in 1796, which led in 1977 to the eradication of smallpox from the earth. The population would flood into the streets and cheer the victory parade of invincible statistics.

They did not. The human frailty of stupidity, irresolution and addiction capitulated to a beaten enemy. Humanity grasped any weapon to defend this craven desertion from its own salvation. My grandma smokes 50 a day at 95 . . . Come off it, you can prove anything by statistics . . . There's no direct link, is there? . . . I'd die without a cigarette . . . Oh, but I'd put on weight!

The association between smoking and slimness precedes the age of dieting:

> To feed on flesh is gluttony.
> It maketh men fat like swine;
> But is not he a frugal man
> That on a loaf can dine?

> He needs no linen for to fowl
> His fingers' ends to wipe,
> That he has his kitchen in a box,
> And roast meat in a pipe.

> The cause wherefore few rich men's sons
> Proved disputants in schools,
> Is that their fathers fed on flesh,
> And they begat fat fools.

> This fulsome feeding clogs the brain
> And doth the stomach choake,
> But he's a brave spark that can dine
> With one light dish of smoke,

sang a *Song in Praise of Tobacco* in 1660.

Over 110,000 Britons are killed by smoking every year, and between one third and one half of all smokers die because of smoking. Captain Cancer is backed up by 30,000 fatal casualties a year from lungs clogged with spit, mostly in smokers. Captain Coronary advances to

142

collect 35,000 corpses a year by blowing them up with heart attacks (fifteen times more hits than in non-smokers), by exploding strokes in their skulls, and by laying arterial land-mines that cut their legs off first. Both Captains warn clearly of their weapons on each cigarette packet, but who takes notice of enemy propaganda?

Such a pathetic surrender is rousingly backed by tobacco companies and governments. The deadly Captains' armourers in Britain are:

American Brands, which owns Gallaher, which has 40 per cent of the British market (Benson and Hedges, Silk Cut), and which makes annual profits of £280 million. The Hanson conglomerate owns Imperial Tobacco, which has 35 per cent (Embassy) and makes £240 million. Rembrandt in South Africa owns Compagnie Financière Richemont in Switzerland, which owns Rothmans, which markets Philip Morris (Marlbro, Raffles) and makes £351 million. The American R. J. Reynolds sells us Camels.

BAT Industries, which makes £966 million a year from tobacco, makes a distribution of 30 million cigarettes a year to Africa and the Far East, where there is a hazier notion among the unsophisticated or unlettered population that they could be killed by them. World casualties from tobacco are 2.5 million a year, and the expected 10 million by 2020 will be reached mostly in the poorer countries. During the famine of the 1970s Ethiopian tobacco consumption rose by 49 per cent, and to withstand the poverty and malnutrition of 1984 Ethiopia imported 200 million British cigarettes.

Shortly after the bomb dropped on Hiroshima, American tobacco companies attacked in the Far East, patriotically reinforced by the US government with cheap loans for the importation of cigarettes. Later, the threat of US trade sanctions exploded Eastern sales to 142 billion, a 24 billion increase in a year. America now has 16 per cent of the Asian market, and has brilliantly succeeded in raising smoking by 5 per cent in one year alone in Taiwan.

Tobacco is the most costly crop in the European Community, attracting a subsidy per hectare thirty-five times that of cereals. In southern Europe, 200,000 tobacco farmers survived in 1988 only on subsidies from Brussels of £724 million, but by 1991 needed £996 million. Nobody in Europe wants to smoke their awful rank, black tobacco, so it is sold cheap to even poorer lands overseas or bestowed upon Russia as humanitarian aid.

'Money is the most important thing in the world,' noted Bernard Shaw in the preface to *Major Barbara*. Even her father, the armaments millionaire Undershaft, might have jibbed at making so much of it not from exuberantly encouraging fellow-humans to kill each other for their ideals, but to commit suicide for their passing pleasure.

The British cigarette companies spend £88 million on advertising, mostly sponsoring sport from motor-racing to cricket, whose stands of spectators could justly be filled with hollow-eyed skeletons. The US tobacco industry supports the Arts. The British government makes £7 billion a year from taxing its voters' smoking, and with the Mad Hatter's self-assurance pays £5 million to try stopping them. Advertising cigarettes in print is banned by France, Italy, Portugal, Finland, Iceland and Norway, but the British government feels that this interferes with the liberty of the Press, to which the Press, which takes the money, earnestly agrees.

Our treacherous government's practice of urging smokers to an early mortuary, for fear of losing its tobacco taxes, is backed by some simple Treasury arithmetic:

A man dying at forty from cancer of the lung had a life expectancy of seventy-five years. He has cost the National Health Service about £2,500 for his unsuccessful thoracic

144

operation (smoking-related diseases cost the NHS £437 million a year), and he will avoid in future paying £21,000 in tax on his national average of six packets of cigarettes a week. Had he not smoked, he would by seventy-five have claimed £30,000 of state retirement pension and cost the NHS at least £5,000 for care in his advancing age. The Government thus shows a profit on a single smoker of £11,500. As 40,000 Britons a year die of lung cancer, encouraging them to develop a single reliably fatal illness saves the Treasury £46 million annually, enough to keep the Arts Council going for almost three months. What the Government cryingly needs, to reduce its vast and increasing welfare debt, is a welcome return of the Black Death.

Any sensible enjoinment to stop people risking their lives with tobacco is countered by articulate blockheads who contend that everyone is at liberty to choose his or her pleasures, and stick their tongues out at the 'nanny society'. Everyone is at liberty to dance along the edge of Beachy Head, and if Eastbourne Council puts up notices saying 'Danger' it cannot be contemptuously dismissed as over-fussy. The nanny society is to blame for furnishing such arguments. It is a widespread human frailty to try to stop people doing what you dislike seeing or imagining them doing, by emphasising its dangers to life, limb, wallet, sexual harmony and eternal salvation. Thus American prohibition failed. But smoking has been proved unarguably fatal for half a century, and anyone who cannot spot the dagger in the do-gooder's cloak risks a deadly thrust.

Tobacco smoke contains 4,000 chemicals, released into the smoker's lungs or into the air for the lungs of others. A cigarette contains 1–6 mg nicotine, a cigar 15–40 mg, and 60 mg of pure nicotine placed on the tongue will kill swiftly not only Culpeper's and Calverley's cat, but you.

Nicotine evaporates in the smoke, 90 per cent of it

absorbed if inhaled, 25–50 per cent absorbed from the mouth, and it reaches the brain in seven seconds. It is ingested from the skin (hence nicotine patches as deterrents). Babies get it richly in their smoking mothers' milk. Nicotine protects against ulcerative colitis and Parkinson's and Alzheimer's diseases. This airs the suggestion that people over the age of sixty should take up smoking, on the original Red Indian curative principle. But it is not beyond pharmacological ingenuity to deliver the nicotine to the gut or brain directly. And why pay taxes on your medicament? Besides, people of sixty starting to smoke may not at all like it.

Nicotine excites then depresses the central nervous system, it increases the heart rate and blood pressure, tones up the bowels and stimulates the adrenal gland to produce adrenalin. It is formidably addictive. Cigarettes, like cars, emit also carbon monoxide, which reduces the oxygen-carrying power of the blood by 15 per cent.

Smokers have been a minority of Britons since 1976. There are now 13.5 million (including the under-sixteen-year-olds, 11 per cent of them regular smokers, spending £90 million a year pocket-money on cigarettes). But 10 million have given up, and the sales of cigarettes fell 25 per cent between 1972 and 1984. The lethal Captains are recognised enemies. Everyone wants to stop. If only they could.

The surest way statistically to stop smoking is social improvement. The percentage of smokers in social class 1 (the nobs with interesting office jobs) is 16, compared with 42 in social class 6 (the blokes with the boring job of digging the road outside). And be a man. Between 1972 and 1984, male smokers dropped by 16 per cent, but female ones by only 9 per cent.

During World War Two, carcinoma of the lung was unknown in women; 50 years afterwards, it is commonplace. Perhaps it started with those cherished scarce

Woodbines from the canteen in the bomber factories. Between 1988 and 1990, it increased in women aged under twenty-five from 28 to 32 per cent. Smoking on the pill heightens the risk of heart and arterial disease ten times; even those eschewing the pill have lighter babies, twice the risk of aborting and the menopause three years early.

An equally worthwhile means of stopping smoking is taking up medicine. Smoking doctors are now curiosities.

The most effective medical advice is simple:

- 1 Smoking is bloody dangerous.
- 2 Smokers are bloody stupid.

So go home and burn all your cigarettes and tobacco in the hearth, chuck in the dustbin your lighters and pipes and ashtrays – save for the silver wedding gift – and like an anonymous alcoholic say: 'I am *not* going to have a cigarette today,' every morning of your lengthened life.

Cigarettes in Britain also ignite annually 6,600 fires, causing 250 deaths.

ELEVEN

# Sharpening the Scythe

The sanctity of life is a human ideal as laughably frail as that of the sanctity of marriage.

For the mass of mankind – to whom Thanatos could be a domestic cleanser – the accusation that we are casually and continually trying to kill ourselves is scoffingly ridiculous. But in the five hundred years since the pox and the pipe were imported from America, man has continued to risk harm from both as cheerfully as from the pot.

The spectres which I have just invoked have long lurked round the feast. 'The first glass for myself, the second for my friends, the third for good humour, and the fourth for mine enemies,' foreboded Sir William Temple, three centuries before death was glimpsed regularly at the bottom of the convivial cup. And Ben Jonson was foreseeing the health hazards of 'that tawney weed' in 1614: 'Hence it is, that the lungs of the tobacconist are rotted, the liver spotted, the brain smok'd like the backside of the pig-woman's booth, here, and the whole body within, black as her pan.'

Some men and women needed to reach beyond the booze and baccy for other self-wounding pleasures.

## The Drowsy Syrups

'It was a Sunday afternoon, wet and cheerless; and a duller spectacle this earth of ours has not to show than a rainy Sunday in London,' De Quincey reasonably justified his taking to opium in 1804.

He was traversing 'the great Mediterranean of Oxford Street', a thoroughfare along which he would later stroll with sentimental memories, 'by dreamy lamplight, and hear those airs played on a common street-organ which years ago solaced me and my dear youthful companion' – who was Ann, an orphan, a fifteen-year-old prostitute.

The man who did for drug addiction what Herman Melville did for whaling was plain Thomas Quincey, son of a bookish Manchester linen merchant with eight children, two of whom swiftly died. Thomas was a dreamy youth, who illuminated his name with 'De' from the nebulous glow of Norman ancestors. In 1802, with his father dead from pulmonary consumption aged thirty-nine, he fled from Manchester Grammar School and wandered round Wales on a guinea a week from his stern and stately mother. Restlessly, he turned to London, where he found squalid if rent-free lodgings at Greek Street in Soho.

At six every evening, on the corner of Oxford Street and Great Titchfield Street, which runs north towards Regent's Park, seventeen-year-old De Quincey met Ann. He had loved her since she had restored him with a glass of port wine and spices, paid from her own purse, in her terror at his suffering a fainting fit in Soho Square.

'Oxford Street, stony-hearted stepmother, thou that listenest to the sighs of orphans, and drinkest the tears of children, at length I was dismissed from thee!' he sentimentalised. From Oxford Street he went to Oxford, and in his first year at Worcester suffered three weeks' excruciating face pain from trigeminal neuralgia, for which a fellow undergraduate recommended opium.

De Quincey had previously vaguely thought of opium as a remote delight like manna or ambrosia. Then, that wet afternoon:

> I saw a druggist's shop. The druggist (unconscious minister of celestial pleasures!), as if in sympathy with the rainy Sunday, looked dull and stupid, just as any mortal druggist might be expected to look on a rainy London Sunday; and when I asked for the tincture of opium, he gave it to me as any other man might do; and, furthermore, out of my shilling returned to me what seemed to be real copper halfpence, taken out of a real wooden drawer. Nevertheless, and notwithstanding all such indications of humanity, he has ever since figured in my mind as a beatific vision of an immortal druggist, sent down to earth on a special mission to myself.

The effect was instant.

> And in an hour, O heavens! what a revulsion! what a resurrection, from its lowest depths of the inner spirit! what an apocalypse of the world within me. That my pains had vanished was now a trifle in my eyes; this negative effect was swallowed up in the immensity of those positive effects which had opened before me, in the abyss of divine enjoyment thus suddenly revealed. Here was a panacea for all human woes; here was the secret of happiness, about which philosophers had disputed for so many ages, at once discovered; happiness might now be bought for a penny, and carried in the waistcoat-pocket; portable ecstasies might be corked up in a pint-bottle; and peace of mind could be sent down by the mail.

After such impulsive and fervent endorsement, De Quincey not surprisingly soon found himself on a daily dose of 12,000 drops of laudanum (laudanum is the tincture, opium dissolved in alcohol). He preferred laudanum because it worked instantly; with solid opium you had to wait four hours before you felt its delights. De Quincey acclaimed opium as the catholic, irresistible anodyne, the potent antidote of nervousness and *tedium vitae*. He was equally certain that it prevented the 'white plague' of pulmonary consumption, with which he had been diagnosed, aged twenty-two, at Humphry Davy's famed Pneumatic Institution at Clifton in the West Country, a diagnosis then usually tantamount to condemnation to death.

After four years, De Quincey found himself down to a daily 300 drops, achieved without even trying; but he relapsed, to peak at 8,000 drops, which he calculated equalled eighty old-fashioned teaspoonfuls, enough for dosing 320 hospital patients. A few times, and for a few months, he made the triumphant effort 'of reconquering my freedom from the yoke of opium'. But he inevitably resumed, at first feeling awful, consoling himself that Lord Nelson, even after the Nile and Copenhagen, was always sick on going back to sea. After fifty-two years, De Quincey stopped taking it. His only reflection was that without opium he would have been in his grave for the past thirty-five of them. He died in Edinburgh three years later, aged seventy-four.

Samuel Taylor Coleridge, who to his Christ's Hospital schoolfellow Charles Lamb was 'an archangel a little damaged', wrote *The Ancient Mariner* when aged twenty-five and an opium addict. He was introduced to laudanum for treatment of rheumatic fever as a schoolboy, and parted from it only on his death aged sixty-one, then a lodger in his doctor's house at Highgate in London. De Quincey became fiercely annoyed at Coleridge's easygoing justification of taking opium for his own rheumatic aches, while Coleridge condemned the drug morally and condemned De Quincey himself as 'an adventurous voluptuary'.

De Quincey reasoned:

> Coleridge's bodily affliction was simple rheumatism. Mine, which intermittingly raged for ten years, was rheumatism of the face combined with toothache . . . Neither rheumatism nor toothache is any *abiding* affection of the system . . . And when the pain ceased, then the opium should have ceased. Why did it not? Because Coleridge had come to taste the genial pleasure of opium . . . That affection which finally drove me into the *habitual* use of opium, what was it? Pain was it? No, but misery. Casual overcasting of sunshine was it? No, but blank desolation. Gloom was it that might have departed? No, but settled and abiding darkness.
>
> . . . total eclipse,
> Without all hope of day!

he ended, bringing in Milton to depict the annihilating mental state that drives frail humanity to drugs.

*The Confessions of an English Opium-Eater* appeared anonymously in 1821 in issues of the *London Magazine*, which published Lamb, Hazlitt, John Clare, Keats, Carlyle and Thomas Hood. Such literary self-exposure created a gratifying sensation. De Quincey became the figurehead of opium addicts, as Dick Turpin of highwaymen and Blackbeard of pirates. But if the early Victorian public ever thought about drug addiction at all, it was of a practice as outlandish and inconsequential as perpetuated by the Montgolfiers' ballooning.

### Poppy Power

Opium is the dried milky juice from the fruit of the poppy *Papaver somniferum*. You incise the pod lightly, choosing the afternoon heat as your time, ten days after the petals have fallen. The next morning, you gather the extruded juice in a poppy-leaf, leaving the seeds inside to ripen for oil.

Opium is a complicated chemical mixture of alkaloids, including the familiar household anodyne, codeine. Morphine is the most powerful of these alkaloids, and the most plentiful: and it is morphine which gives opium its effect. When De Quincey's *Confessions* were serialised, the sprouting opium trade was about to flourish as luxuriantly as the two-foot-high white poppies of India and Turkey which fed it. And the trade throughout the world was controlled by Britain.

Britain was then, in the 1820s, annually importing 90,000 pounds of opium and re-exporting half. By 1880, Britain was importing 650,000 pounds, and continued absorbing this bulk until 1920, re-exporting 300,000 pounds a year until the Great War. A third of these exports went to America, which was importing one pound per 1,000 population in 1840, and five pounds per 1,000 in 1855. The world's opium gluttons were the Chinese.

The British East India Company ran an efficient department to export Indian opium, processed in Britain, into China, where opium was prohibited. The trade, though regrettably illicit, was so profitable that it provided 18 per cent of the Indian Government's revenue. The British themselves preferred Turkish opium, which contained 10 per cent morphine, twice the Indian level. The Turks responded by buying with equal eagerness Lancashire cottons and Yorkshire woollens, while the British Government benevolently reduced the opium import duty steadily from nine shillings a pound in De Quincey's heyday to nil at his death.

The business operated from Mincing Lane, which runs north from Eastcheap near the Tower of London. Mincing

Lane controlled also the world's tea trade, which brought fragrant Orange Pekoe and Darjeeling and Lapsang Souchong to the delicate Wedgwood cups of English ladies' firesides. It was the opium re-exported to China which paid for their tea.

The East India Company, so expert at handling Chinese smugglers and slippery officials, in 1834 lost its monopoly to the British Crown, which was not. The forbidden opium was held in storeships that sailed from Bengal and hove-to off the Canton river – like the 'Rum Row' Atlantic fleet during American prohibition – and was then sold over the side into smugglers' boats. In 1840, the first Opium War broke out. The Chinese had surrounded the British ashore with troops, demanded that the storeships be unloaded, and destroyed 20,000 chests of opium. The fat profits from opium had been camouflaged by Foreign Secretary Lord Palmerston under the moral necessity for free trade, which this unmannerly Chinese action disrupted.

An expeditionary force was dispatched from India, and the Chinese, who mildly complained that the British were 'unaware of the necessity of conforming to the laws of the Celestial Empire', ended up in 1842 beaten and having to cede Hong Kong to Queen Victoria. There was another Opium War in 1856–60, in which Peking was captured. More Chinese ports were forced open to British trade. This could henceforth provide China with opium, and Mincing Lane with profits, in an equally enjoyable and stainlessly legal manner.

After rarefied De Quincey, the opium addict became a solid literary decoration. In 1870, Dickens's unfinished *Edwin Drood* began:

He is in the meanest and closest of small rooms.
Through the ragged window-curtain, the light of early
day steals in from a miserable court. He lies, dressed,

across a large unseemly bed, upon a bedstead that has indeed given way under the weight upon it. Lying, also dressed and also across the bed, not longwise, are a Chinaman, a Lascar, and a haggard woman. The two first are in a sleep or stupor; the last is blowing at a kind of pipe, to kindle it. And as she blows, and, shading it with her lean hand, concentrates its red spark of light, it serves in the dim morning as a lamp to show him what he sees of her.

'Another?' says this woman, in a querulous rattling whisper. 'Have another?'

He looks about him, with his hand to his forehead.

'Ye've smoked as many as five since ye came in at midnight,' the woman goes on, as she chronically complains. 'Poor me, poor me, my head is so bad. Them two come in after ye. Ah, poor me, the business is slack, is slack! Few Chinamen about the Docks, and fewer Lascars, and no ships coming in, these say! Here's another ready for ye, deary. Ye'll remember like a good soul, won't ye, that the market price is dreffle high just now? More nor three shillings and sixpence for a thimbleful! And ye'll remember that nobody by me (and Jack Chinaman t'other side of the court; be he can't do it as well as me) has the true secret of mixing it? Ye'll pay up accordingly, deary, won't ye?'

She blows at the pipe as she speaks, and, occasionally bubbling at it, inhales much of its contents.

Twenty years later, in Oscar Wilde's *Picture of Dorian Gray*:

Suddenly the man drew up with a jerk at the top of a dark lane. Over the low roofs and jagged chimney-stacks of the houses rose the black mass of ships. Wreathes of white mist clung like ghostly sails to the yards.

'Somewhere about here, sir, ain't it?' he asked huskily through the trap.

Dorian started, and peered round. 'This will do,' he answered, and, having got out hastily, and given the

**155**

driver the extra fare he had promised him, he walked quickly in the direction of the quay. Here and there a lantern gleamed at the stern of some huge merchantman. The light shook and splintered in the puddles. A red glare came from an outward-bound steamer that was coaling. The slimy pavement looked like a wet mackintosh.

He hurried on towards the left, glancing back now and then to see if he was being followed. In about seven or eight minutes he reached a small shabby house, that was wedged in between two gaunt factories. In one of the top windows stood a lamp. He stopped, and gave a peculiar knock.

After a little time he heard steps in the passage, and the chain being unhooked. The door opened quietly, and he went in without saying a word to the squat misshapen figure that flattened itself into the shadow as he passed. At the end of the hall hung a tattered green curtain that swayed and shook in the gusty wind which had followed him in from the street. He dragged it aside, and entered a long, low room which looked as if it had once been a third-rate dancing-saloon. Shrill flaring gas-jets, dulled and distorted in the fly-blown mirrors that faced them, were ranged round the walls. Greasy reflectors of ribbed tin backed them, making quivering disks of light. The floor was covered with ochre-coloured sawdust, trampled here and there into mud, and stained with rings of spilt liquor. Some Malays were crouching by a little charcoal stove playing with bone counters, and showing their white teeth as they chatted. In one corner with his head buried in his arms, a sailor sprawled over a table, and by the tawdrily painted bar that ran across one complete side stood two haggard women mocking an old man who was brushing the sleeves of his coat with an expression of disgust. 'He thinks he's got red ants on him,' laughed one of them, as Dorian passed by. The man looked at her in terror, and began to whimper.

At the end of the room was a little staircase, leading to a darkened chamber. As Dorian hurried up its three rickety steps, the heavy odour of opium met him. He

**156**

heaved a deep breath, and his nostrils quivered with pleasure. When he entered, a young man with smooth yellow hair, who was bending over a lamp lighting a long thin pipe, looked up at him, and nodded in a hesitating manner.

'You here, Adrian?' muttered Dorian.

'Where else should I be?' he answered listlessly. 'None of the chaps will speak to me now.'

Dorian Gray had just committed a murder.

Such agreeably shocking behaviour of the better classes was set too picturesquely for the seemly reality of London's few 'opium dens' in Limehouse near the docks. And these must have been few, because in 1861 there were only 665 Chinese in the whole of Britain. They smoked opium from eighteen-inch-long bamboo pipes, their iron bowls the size of half a pigeon's egg. The sticky opium was first flamed on a needle at a lamp, and its vapour was inhaled until it burnt out. This was performed amid chatting and gambling and furniture and tea, all as decorous as a Chinese social club.

Dickens had seen an East End den, but needed the tarnish of melodrama. He took laudanum himself, as did Keats, Walter Scott, Wilkie Collins and Elizabeth Barrett Browning. It sustained them while writing, but it did not merit their excuse of bettering the result. As Florence Nightingale noticed, when home from Scutari and (as usual anticipating the progress of medicine) effecting opium implants with a silver knife under the skin of her thigh: 'It does not improve the vivacity or serenity of one's intellect.'

The effects of morphine – effectively, the effects of the ripening poppy's opium – are:

– Pain-killing.
– Drowsiness.
– Euphoria.

– Pin-point pupils.
– Relief of acute heart failure.
– Depressing respiration.
– Suppressing coughing.
– Vomiting.
– Calming the guts.

The relief of pain and anguish, and the postponement of death, are the doctors' two Articles of Religion. For exorcising pain, there was nothing like opium. 'God's own medicine', opium was appreciated by grandee Edwardian physician Sir William Osler. Thomas Sydenham, one of Cromwell's captains of horse who became one of Oxford's most sensible physicians and the 'English Hippocrates', decided justly that 'few would be willing to practise medicine without opium'. He himself bestowed it generously in 'Sydenham's laudanum', made all the more welcome by being spiced with saffron, cinnamon and cloves.

The action of morphine is swift, direct, obvious, unfailing and unique, though demanding mounting doses. It assuages the pain that is stopped only by death. It fortifies patients before operations. It strengthened the Victorians' cough mixtures and stopped their diarrhoea. Thus it became a desperate remedy for the oft-fatal cholera, which was endemic in India and epidemic in Britain.

In the middle of the nineteenth century, opium became the religion of the people.

### Cure Guaranteed

Dr J. Collis Browne had served on the Army Medical Staff in India, and in 1848 had prescribed a mixture of opium and chloroform for the country's incessant cholera. It was a disease as mysterious as it was frightening. Before Dr

Robert Koch, out East with the Cholera Commission from Germany, discovered down the microscope the comma-shaped, highly motile *Vibrio cholerae* germ in 1883, nobody knew that the infection was transmitted from one human to another through their faeces, by water, food and flies.

There was cholera aplenty in Britain. Home on leave in 1854, Dr J. Collis Browne tried his medicine on an outbreak in Trimdon, a stricken village near Durham. When he retired from the Army two years later, he named the mixture Chlorodyne and sold the rights to a Blooms-bury chemist, who dispensed it in shilling bottles as a cure for cholera, diarrhoea, colic, flatulence, stomach chills, coughs, colds, flu, bronchitis, croup, whooping-cough, cramps, neuralgia, rheumatism and sleeplessness.

Customers were soon buying it in dozens, like the beer. It cheered everybody up wonderfully, even if unfortunately everybody found that they needed to take more and more for the same effect. Rivals to Dr J. Collis Browne flooded the market deliciously with opium, either dubiously curative like Black Drop, or as honest 'pick-me-ups' and 'nerve tonics' such as Fire Brigade Mixture and Eucomen (which contained 40 per cent alcohol as well). Godfrey's Cordial, Mrs Winslow's Soothing Syrup and Infants' Quietness were mixtures of opium in sweet syrup, recommended for restless children. These were so effective that mothers everywhere were enjoying unbroken nights, or days of gainful work, by abandoning their offspring in their cots in states of opiate stupor. It was so much cheaper than a nanny.

People began to think they should be doing something about this. Moralistic busybodying is a practical and sometimes useful human frailty.

In 1871, Dr J. Collis Browne's Chlorodyne took £28,415, and Britain suffered ninety-six deaths from accidental opium poisoning (thirty-nine of the fatalities under the age of five), which were 27.5 per cent of all deaths from accidental poisonings. There were also eleven opiate suicides, which were 8.3 per cent of all suicides by poisons. These statistics are shaky, because opium poisoning could be muddled by the doctor with natural death as easily as the reverse.

More reliably, infant mortality was about 25 per 100,000 in the thriving industrial towns of Manchester and Wolverhampton. Local chemists there were selling twenty gallons of Godfrey's Cordial a year. The Ladies Sanitary Association was becoming outraged at the economics of working-class mothers doping their infants at threepence an ounce, then abandoning them to go out to work for fifteen shillings a week. Or the mothers could accumulate their tots at two shillings a week with daily childminders, who immediately opiated the lot.

This horror was largely as imaginary as the Limehouse opium dens. Most factory girls were under twenty-one, and renounced their factories on marriage. If they went on working, they became domestics, with their child alongside. And if they did not work, the child was underfed. In the middle class, it was the parents who needed soothing against 'teething' (i.e., normally irritating) children. The advertisement for Mrs Winslow's Soothing Syrup had a handsome, stylishly nightied mum in bed with two narcotised angels.

The Fens had a famed, odd avidity for opium, which made fortunes for the chemists of King's Lynn and Downham Market. The stretch from Cambridge to the Wash consumed half England's opium imports. Perhaps it was to counter the miasmas from the marshes, which everybody since the Romans knew to cause the agues of malaria, for which their buzzing mosquitoes had not yet been convicted.

The British Poisons and Pharmacy Act of 1868 established pharmacists as the only sellers of dangerous drugs,

160

as the Medical Act of 1858 made the General Medical Council's registered doctors the only providers of medical care. But the pharmacists could still sell opium over the counter to anyone they liked, so long as it had POISON on the bottle. In 1892, Dr J. Collis Browne's Chlorodyne was forced to don this label, which stark description reduced its sales by 13 per cent. The only other necessity was a patent medicine's tax stamp, which brought the government an income as welcome, and as reliable, as do cigarettes today.

In 1908, another Act restricted pharmacists to selling opium only to customers they knew, or to their friends, but Dr J. Collis Browne's was still making £25,000 a year and 126 people were still dying annually from opium poisoning. The best part of a century passed before Dr J. Collis Browne's mixture was purged of opium. By then, the British government was becoming worried about the 25 million prescriptions it was paying for yearly to tranquillise its eternally edgy population with more sophisticated drugs.

### Forbidden Foliage

In America, moralistic busybodying is like Niagara compared with the splash of Britain's biggest, the Fairy Glen Falls at Betws-y-Coed.

America grew concerned about the Chinese smoking opium. The more progressive Chinese had already turned to injecting morphine, which had been introduced by British doctors as a cure for opium smoking. Morphine was delightedly discovered to be faster and cheaper, though its injectors in the Soochow teashops used a single syringe and did not even wipe the needle between customers, so setting an infective peril inherited by Aids.

America convened a conference in Shanghai in 1909 to

halt the bustling Far East opium traffic. In the mid-nineteenth century, America had been making $2 million a year from the Chinese opium trade, but this had fallen sufficiently to permit such an expression of high principles. The Americans were earnestly joined by the British Government, which had been goaded by the Quakers' Society for the Suppression of the Opium Trade since 1874, and by the Women's Anti-Opium Urgency League since 1891. The British Indian opium revenues had fallen equally disastrously.

The Germans joined in, though worried about the freedom of cocaine flowing from their own flourishing drug industry (they had been pushing opium's shadow, aspirin, since 1899). An International Opium Convention was cemented in The Hague in 1912, but it invited tardy ratification, and by 1914 the signatories had worse to worry about.

In 1914, the Harrison Act controlled narcotic drugs in America. In Britain, the sale of opium was regulated and restricted in 1916, in the native way by a regulation under the Defence of the Realm Act – the familiar DORA – which had been passed by Parliament for matters entirely different. An incitement was forty Canadian soldiers in Folkestone discovered to be drug addicts. The DORA regulation was demobilised in 1920 as the Dangerous Drugs Act, which effected a brilliant, if unnoticed, alliance of the newborn Ministry of Health and the Home Office who ran the police, and was passed by Parliament with resounding apathy. An incitement was the lovely popular actress Billie Carleton, who smoked opium *déshabillé* in the early hours, and died after the Victory Ball at the Albert Hall in November 1918, most unpatriotically, it was thought.

Billie Carleton speeded her end by also injecting heroin and sniffing cocaine, two drugs which incited the 'dope fiends' of the twenties and thirties, always suspectedly

162

supplied by the Chinese. Heroin is diamorphine, created by the German drug company Bayer in 1898. It is a stronger and faster pain-killer than morphine, providing a yearned-for feeling of 'cocooned warmth'. A few smart people were sensationalised over cocaine by the newspapers, though the workers and the prostitutes, who paid ten shillings a packet for it, did not merit such trouble (a fifth of cocaine arrests were of women). The fiends were mythologised by Sax (*Fu Manchu*) Rohmer's novels and by Sherlock Holmes's propensities, by Noël Coward's *The Vortex* of 1928 and vividly (if initially silently) by movies such as *Frailty* in 1921.

Heroin can be given effectively by mouth. This way is now particulary favoured in terminal illness, laced with cocaine and perhaps gin – the 'Hospice Cocktail', everyman's hemlock.

Cocaine affords exciting delusions of strength, stamina and superiority. It comes from the coca bush, its leaves having been chewed by eight centuries of Peruvians and Bolivians to ward off fatigue and hunger. They buttered the leaves with lime, because alkali betters the extraction of the drug. In 1862, more German chemists had produced from the coca leaf its pure alkaloid, which in 1884 became the first local anaesthetic. The budding young Viennese eye surgeon Carl Koller had been enjoyably swallowing cocaine, and noticing that it numbed the tongue on the way down wondered if it would usefully numb the eye. It did instantly, on a handy laboratory frog which he seized in a cloth, and which allowed him to poke its cocainised bulging eye without jumping out.

Koller had been experimenting on cocaine in the Vienna General Hospital lab with young Sigmund Freud, who was a cocaine enthusiast, declaring that it filled him with energy and prevented indigestion. He was recommending it to everyone, particulary his fiancée Martha, 'to make her strong and give her cheeks a red colour' (he had noticed that it caused also 'violent sexual excitement'). Freud continued swallowing cocaine in a world which vaguely noticed it as a fashionable and recherché stimulant. This was perhaps because he prissily disliked 'the faint mental obfuscation that even a slight drink induces'.

Doctors became as enthusiastic self-dosers with cocaine as with opium. And like opium, cocaine fortified patent medicines which were advertised to cure anything from the common cold to consumption. Binney's Catarrh Snuff was wildly popular in America in 1900, its fanciers buying six bottles a day. A Corsican chemist's Vin Mariani, endorsed by Buffalo Bill, Queen Victoria and the world's elect in state, church, or art, was thick with cocaine.

The Queen herself ordered from the local Balmoral pharmacy hefty supplies of cocaine, heroin, chloroform and adrenalin. Her guests had cocaine-and-menthol lozenges to suck and the Princess Royal rubbed it in. Nobody thought twice about it. In 1896, Coca Cola provided cocaine as a tonic for the elderly, but ten years later thought better of it and flourished on the cola alone. Today's 'crack' is crystalline cocaine, smokable, a tenth of the price. Cannabis Indica – also called Indian hemp, hashish, gunjah, ganga, charas, daga, marijuana or bhang – has been chewed by the Assyrians since 700 BC and smoked by the Americans since 1910.

Under the British Dangerous Drugs Act, 300 people were prosecuted for using various drugs in 1923, but only fifty in 1920, which was only forty-six more than the police 'drugs squad'. The drug menace seemed to have faded like the dragons of opiate dreams. In America, the dragon breathed fire the fiercer. During the 1930s, the Federal Bureau of Narcotics had 150 employees and a $1 million budget and brought between 3,000 and 7,000 prosecutions a year. Drug addiction was then complicated by prohibition, which pushed the desperately susceptible from one illegal stimulant to another.

The Americans anyway saw drugging, like drinking, as sinning first and sickening next. The British let the addict go on getting his drug from his doctor. The Americans forced him to get it from criminals. 'The Real McCoy' was Whiffen's morphia, from the biggest British manufacturers, who had trebled their output during the war, though much of it ended not in the field hospitals of France but in China. Whiffen's was complimented by its name being forged on countless bottles, until the maker's licence was revoked by a suspicious British government in 1923.

For the past quarter-century we have had no 'drug addicts'. The World Health Organisation prefers, with its habitual verbosity, the term 'drug dependence', which is:

> . . . a state, psychic and sometimes physical, resulting
> from the interaction between a living organism and a
> drug, characterised by behavioural and other
> responses that always include a compulsion to take
> the drug on a continuous or periodic basis in order to
> experience its psychic effects, and sometimes to avoid
> the discomfort of its absence.

Such dependence arising from the lovely feelings inspired by the drug, and by the dislike of losing them, is augmented by the specifically nasty effects of stopping. With morphine, this is a week of sweating, vomiting, diarrhoea, cramps, sleeplessness, anxiety, weeping and goose-flesh (the 'cold turkey'). But withdrawing cocaine is painless. The world's drug takers are mostly immature and feckless, mixing comfortingly with others doing the same, males to females 8 to 1, often delinquent, and progressing to using more and more of different drugs. Britain in 1993 had 24,700 addicts, 9,700 of them new that year, half injecting themselves, mostly men under

**165**

thirty, and mostly in London, though Merseyside is catching up. In America, 6 per cent of the population are addicts, with 1.2 million on cocaine alone.

Drugs in Britain in 1990 caused 1,263 deaths: 294 from using the drug, 233 from accidental poisoning, 440 from suicide, 262 from obscure reasons, and 24 from Aids. Such figures are as unreliable as the Victorians', because they depend on the addict seeing the doctor, the doctor making the correct diagnosis, and then conscientiously notifying the Home Office. The nation's drug addicts increased by 13 per cent in 1988, when the doctors were reminded of this obligation.

The 1,605 heroin and 860 cocaine users caught in the act in 1990 were sweepingly outnumbered by the 40,194 nabbed with cannabis, which is smoked by a third of a million Britons as a mild relaxant. Less wickedly, there are tranquillisers to slow you down, amphetamine to speed you up, and everyday solvents to inhale. But solvents kill a hundred a year, more than any single drug.

The world today supports a flourishing drug traffic, which flows along routes as robustly charted as the voyage from India to Britain and back to China in the days when Victoria was Empress. Cocaine grown in Peru and extracted in Colombia is showered in small planes upon Mexico and the Bahamas, for dispatch by car or boat to the United States. Poppies grown in remote northern Afghanistan, and the far Khyber region of Pakistan, form the springs of a narcotic stream which runs from Turkey through Bulgaria, Romania and Hungary or Italy to Austria. The fare rises from $150 a kilo across the Iran–Turkish border to $1,500 on reaching the *autostrada*.

The world produces annually 400 tonnes of heroin and 700 tonnes of cocaine, selling at $15 a gram in the US and double that in Europe, with only 10 per cent of it ending in the arms of the law. Drugs provide a livelihood for one and a half million people. The yearly income from trafficking is $500 billion, 50 per cent of it profit, pleasantly untaxed. The national economies of the producing countries have become as hopelessly dependent on the regular supply of drugs as have the addicts. In the politically unstable ones, the export of illicit drugs has financed the import of illicit weapons. Politicians are against drugs, as preachers are against sin, but:

> Politicians must be challenged on the genuineness of their commitment to the welfare of the planet and for once should put politics aside. Unless they put their wallets *and* their hands on their hearts, the 'war on drugs' will remain exactly as the phrase appears – empty and lost.

So lamely ends one exhaustive study of global drug trafficking.


### A Dose of Death

But is the righteous war against the right enemy?

Under 300 Britons a year die from drugs. From drink, between 5,000 and 25,000 die a year – nobody seems capable of a sober calculation. Over 100,000 die from smoking, according to the Royal College of Physicians. Projecting this proportion, the 3,000,000 who die every year from tobacco throughout the world are matched by a mere 9,000 dying from drugs.

The reasons for drugs – and, once, drink – facing prohibition are:

- Their giving pleasure.
- Their provoking peculiar and occasionally dangerous behaviour.
- Their destabilising of personalities.

**167**

– All this exciting their opponents to indulge in the enjoyable human frailty of moral outrage.

The single reason that tobacco does not face banning is that it ruins no lives and breaks no bones or homes until it kills you.

The supply and the use of drugs is criminal in America. In Holland, the use is not. Dutch law shuns moral values but encourages practical ones. It tries to lessen the harm to drug users, which the Dutch decided that their prosecution would increase rather than solve.

I have a proposal of Swiftian modesty. Drugs, like drink, should be free for all, but tobacco outlawed. It would still be grown in remote clandestine crops, and subjected to the experienced enforcers of authority. Hunting contraband tobacco would create hardly more disruption among the world's police and customs than retraining a few sniffer dogs. Smokers would be jailed, and Malaysian tobacconists cheerfully hanged.

Only a few smokers would follow the Americans who under prohibition took heavily to dangerous drugs: they would be too frightened. Nor would they drink more instead: the effect of alcohol and of its complementary cigarette are so different. Many would switch to marijuana: but the third of a million Britons who have done so already make comparatively little nuisance of themselves.

We should instead acclaim the resurrection of Dr J. Collis Browne, in his Victorian vigour. A few swallowers of mild opium mixtures would overdose themselves, a few suicidal humans would use opium instead of something else, but a leeway of deaths of 2,991,000 a year more than recommends or justifies the experiment. It demands it.

Most drug users, being as intelligent and respectable as most smokers, would not overdo their pleasure. They would be discovered to be as decorous as De Quincey and Coleridge, Dickens and Freud. The drug problem would be eliminated by the sensible recognition that it never existed.

What political St George will make the dragon vanish?

# TWELVE

# A Chapter of Accidents

Man displays an incredible carelessness towards the easeful appliances with which he ingeniously surrounds himself.

Ninety per cent of accidents are caused by human frailty, according to the Royal Society for the Prevention of Accidents, which since its foundation in 1916 has made little impact on this daunting self-proclaimed task.

Here are four famous examples.

### The Unsinkable

Twenty minutes before eight bells were expected to ring from the foredeck, signalling the changing of the night watch to the middle watch at midnight on Sunday, 14 April 1912, the two lookouts in the crow's-nest forty feet up the foremast, ahead of the bridge and the four funnels of the *Titanic*, on a freezing, dead calm, star-glittering night, spied an iceberg across the prow. When they had reported for duty on the night watch an hour after dusk, the men had been warned by the bridge that ice was about. On the bridge now, thirty feet below them, the *Titanic*'s first officer in command of the watch – his binoculars to hand – and the quartermaster in his bell-bottoms and round sailor's hat at the wheel, both saw nothing beyond the binnacle. The captain, like Drake, was sleepin' there below.

The crow's-nest ship's bell would clang conventionally once for danger to port, twice for starboard, and three times for dead ahead, which it now alarmingly announced. Half a minute later, with the ship's wheel put hard to turn a-port and the engine-room telegraph ringing full astern, the 66,000-ton, 300-yard-long, exuberantly acclaimed luxurious *Titanic*, on her maiden voyage from Southampton to New York, grazed the underwater ice at 25 m.p.h., ripping her hull below the water-line.

Thus a massive iceberg was first sighted on a clear night only 350 yards ahead of the bow. This is seamanship comparable to the Jumblies going to sea in a Sieve. The *Titanic* sank two hours and forty minutes later into the Atlantic at 41 N by 50 W, the latitude of Madrid. Having lifeboats for only 1,178 of the 2,207 crew and passengers – many of these passengers being delightfully and enviably rich – she lost 1,502 lives and inaugurated an unfading legend of Biblical-sized retribution for man's self-proclaimed magnificence.

The *Titanic* suffered a treacherous design fault.

With seamanlike promptitude, all her emergency doors were shut by electricity before the impact. But the ship was gashed along the starboard edge of the foremost six of her sixteen watertight compartments, which were formed by bulkheads running athwartships across the hull. As these compartments did not ascend above the lowermost decks, the flooding inrush overtopped them. She filled and sank like a cracked basin. Her designers anticipated the perilous complacency exhibited in the crow's-nest and on the bridge, by envisaging no collision with a ship or Manhattan pier ever piercing more than two of her watertight slices, with which she could disdainfully stay afloat. So they defined the *Titanic* as unsinkable.

The two lookouts who sank the ship survived. Had the pair, and their shipmates manning the bridge, been reasonably sharp-eyed and attentive seamen, had they sighted the iceberg a little further away than their own ship's length, the speedy *Titanic* would have survived the Kaiser's U-boats and not until rusty old age gone to her breaker. We should have lost the spectacular indulgence in another human frailty, that of enjoying the (even fatal) come-uppance of people privileged to travel through life first class.

### The Deflatable

Eighteen and a half years later, Britain's airborne *Titanic* was the airship R 101. She was filled with instantly inflammable hydrogen, confined in gas-bags the size of Westminster Hall, which were made of glycerine-soaked, stuck-together sheets of bovine intestine, ordered specially from the canning plants of Chicago. It took a million bullocks to get the R 101 airborne.

The airship was longer than the crack Atlantic liner *Mauretania*, and almost three-quarters the length of the vanished *Titanic*. Its double-bunked passenger cabins were electrically lit through artificial ship's portholes, the dining-saloon could serve hot meals for sixty, and everyone enjoyed unbroken light music through the wireless loudspeakers. The promenade deck sported a ship's rail and provided deckchairs for admiring the view. The lounge was the size of a tennis-court with ferns and palms in pots, and the lightweight wicker furniture was rearrangeable every evening for dancing.

*En route* from Bedfordshire to India, the airship hit a

wooded hill near Beauvais in northern France at five past two on a stormy October Sunday morning and exploded.

The first leg of so breathtakingly imaginative a voyage for 1930 was to Cairo, timed for thirty-six hours. The airship had got as far as Beauvais at 35 m.p.h., almost scraping the roofs and spires on the way: 'The R 101 is coming down the drive,' announced an agitated butler, interrupting dinner at a hilltop Sussex country house. At dinner in Chequers that evening, the Prime Minister, Ramsay MacDonald, had confessed in his rambling way: 'I am still uneasy. My apprehension for unlooked-for danger and disaster, ridiculous, no doubt, and admittedly without the smallest bias in personal knowledge of individual experience, will not be set at rest until I know for a fact that the great airship has safely arrived in India.'

Forty-eight of the fifty-four aboard were killed, including Lord Thomson, the Secretary of State for Air, who, though displaying to the world his confidence in the airship, had prudently made his will and insured his life the night before leaving. Lord Thomson had needed speedily to return to London within a fortnight, to make a gloriously prompt entrance at the Imperial Conference. Thus it was a matter of British prestige getting the R 101 off on time, and in 1930, with Gandhi imprisoned at the airship's destination and his supporters running riot, British prestige needed it.

'The R 101 started for India before she could be regarded as having emerged successfully from all the exhaustive tests proper to an experimental stage,' later condemned the Inquiry Report in London. 'It is impossible to avoid the conclusion that the R 101 would not have started for India on the evening of October 4 if it had not been that reasons of public policy were considered as making it highly desirable for her to do so if she could.'

The impatience and carelessness which caused the

crash were incited by politicians' recklessness in applying ignorance to expediency. The German airship *Hindenburg* decisively confirmed on 6 May 1937, by blowing up and burning out in five minutes while docking in New York and killing the thirty-five aboard, that any aircraft filled with seven million cubic feet of violently explosive gas exhibits the frailty of human inventiveness initiated by Icarus.

## The Irascible

The Forces of the Crown are as accident-prone as those whom they defend, and enjoy the ready use of apparatus swiftly and powerfully to express it.

On 22 June 1893, the Royal Navy's Mediterranean Fleet on summer manoeuvres – nine battleships and four cruisers – sailing from Beirut in two columns at the speed of a bicycle, arrived sixty miles away at Tripoli Bay in Syria at half-past three on a lovely afternoon. The 10,600-ton battleship HMS *Camperdown*, leading one column, then rammed the starboard side of the flagship HMS *Victoria* leading the other. Her engines already full astern in panic, *Camperdown* backed off and let the sea flood into her victim. *Victoria* capsized and sank in five minutes in eighty-seven fathoms of water, taking down the Fleet's commander Vice-Admiral Sir George Tryon and 358 of her crew, her screws still churning and still flying the unworried signal 'Negative send boats'.

Aristocratic Tryon was a difficult admiral. He wished to shake up the Royal Navy, which had been sailing on largely unruffled waters since Trafalgar. At twenty-nine he had commanded *Warrior*, the first British sea-going ironclad. He had invented a new system of signalling for the yeomen's hoisting. He had organised the defence of Australia. He had besieged Sebastopol. The Mediterranean Fleet was already the innovatory squadron of the Royal Navy, and Tryon continued an enthusiastic experimenter. He considered his second-in-command, teetotal, middle-class, fussy Rear-Admiral Albert Markham aboard *Camperdown*, as incompetent and shaky, and often told him so.

The accident occurred three and a quarter minutes after *Victoria*'s helm had been put over, in execution of Tryon's order for a fancy manoeuvre seven miles off the coast. He was transforming the two close-abreast columns into four, which, turned through ninety degrees, would steam spectacularly to their anchorage and impress the natives.

The first move was for both columns to swing inwards, a command which so alarmed Rear-Admiral Markham that he hesitated to comply. This brought a furious flutter from the flagship's yardarm: 'What are you waiting for?' Markham shruggingly supposed that his commander's scintillating seamanship would set the turning circle of *Victoria* safely outside the course of *Camperdown*, and did his duty.

Vice-Admiral Tryon had not noticed that his plan would inevitably bring the leading ships into collision. No one at Rear-Admiral Markham's court martial at Malta could suggest why the Vice-Admiral had overlooked this. Perhaps Tryon was off-colour from Malta fever, caught from the local goats' milk. This had infected Commander Jellicoe, who swam away sick from his bunk aboard *Victoria*, later to oversee the Battle of Jutland. Or perhaps it was the vintage port after Tryon's solitary lunch. Markham got his sword back from the court.

## The Unavoidable

On Wednesday, 15 September 1830, William Huskisson, MP for Liverpool, a free trader and Catholic emancipator, once a minister under Pitt and recently Leader of the House of Commons under the Duke of Wellington, until he resigned in a squabble over Parliamentary seats, was enjoying the opening of the world's first passenger railway.

It ran from Liverpool to Manchester, double-track, and the 31-mile trip took ninety minutes. America needed to wait until that Christmas Day for the 'Best Friend of Charleston' to puff its first cars across six miles of South Carolina.

The man from *The Times* 'had intended to give you some faint description of this astounding work of art, of the crowds which lined almost every inch of our road, of the flags and banners, the booths and scaffoldings, and gorgeous tents', when this happened:

> Mr Huskisson was discoursing with Mr Joseph Sandars, one of the principal originators and promoters of this railroad, and was congratulating that gentleman as one of the happiest men in the world, in having seen a work of such importance and magnitude happily brought to a conclusion under his auspices, when he was called away to speak with some other gentlemen, who were anxious to hear his opinion on some details of the road. Before he left Mr Sandars, he said to that gentleman, 'Well I must go and shake hands with the Duke [of Wellington] on this day at any rate.' The gentlemen who had called him away detained him some time, and whilst he was standing with them, the *Rocket* engine, which, like the *Phoenix*, had to pass the Duke's car, to take up its station at the watering place, came slowly up, and as the engineer had been for some time checking its velocity, so silently that it was almost upon the group before they observed it. In the hurry of the moment all

attempted to get out of the way. Mr Holmes MP, who was standing by the side of Mr Huskisson, desired the gentlemen not to stir, but to cling close by the side of their own car – most excellent advice, had it been followed – for as no engine can move off the rail, any person who stands clear of it is perfectly safe from danger. Unfortunately, in the hurry and agitation of the moment, Mr Huskisson did not pursue this advice. He hesitated, staggered a little as if not knowing what to do, then attempted to run forward, found it impossible to get off the road, on account of an excavation of some 14 or 15 feet depth being on that side of it on which he was, attempted again to get into the car, was hit by a motion of the door as he was mounting a step, and was thrown directly in the path of the *Rocket*, as that engine came opposite to the Duke's car. He contrived to move himself a little out of its path before it came in contact with him, otherwise it must have gone directly over his head and breast. As it was, the wheel went over his left thigh, squeezing it almost to a jelly, broke the leg, it is said, in two places, laid the muscles bare from the ankle nearly to the hip, and tore out a large piece of flesh as it left him. Mrs Huskisson, who, along with several other ladies, witnessed the accident, uttered a shriek of agony, which none who heard will ever forget. As soon as Mr Huskisson could be raised from the ground, he asked where Mrs Huskisson was, and in the most cool and collected manner gave such directions as he thought best fitted for the situation in which he was placed. Mrs Huskisson was immediately by his side to attend to his wishes, but was soon obliged to give way to Dr Brandreth, who applied a tourniquet to stop the dreadful effusion of blood under which Mr Huskisson was suffering. In a few minutes afterwards Mr Huskisson fainted away, and in that condition was removed, as carefully as circumstances would allow, into the car, in which the band of music preceding the Duke's car had been placed. The musicians were immediately turned out of it, and Mrs Huskisson, Mr Wainewright (Mr Huskisson's private secretary), and several other of Mr Huskisson's friends took their places. The Duke's car was detached from the *Northumbrian* engine and fastened laterally to the two engines *Phoenix* and *North Star*. The *Northumbrian* engine then having no other weight to draw but the car which had carried the band, and was now occupied by Mr Huskisson and his party, proceeded at a rapid rate to Manchester to procure medical assistance. As it passed by our car Mr Huskisson was laid at the bottom of it, pale and ghostly as death, and his wife was hanging over him in an agony of tears.

Poor Mr Huskisson! He died the same day.

The balloonist Pilâtre de Rozier had already the grisly distinction of being the world's first airborne fatality, crashing in flames on the Channel coast while crossing from Boulogne to England on 15 June 1785. Mr Huskisson led the mangled procession of victims from railway accidents. *The Times'* index for that quarter of 1830 perpetuates his strange bedfellows in accidental misery:

- Mrs Diana Andrews, run over and Killed by a Stage Coach, at Kensington.
- Boat Upset on the Ouse, and Seven Persons Drowned.
- Brazier, an Old Man, who while Brewing at his Masters, of Moulsham Lodge, fell backwards into the Wort Tub and afterwards Died from the Scalding.
- Mr Edwards, his Wife and a Boatman, Drowned at Ipswich.
- Mr Enticknap, Shot by his Servant, by Accident.
- Dr Gray, Bishop of Bristol, from the Sleeve of his Robe taking Fire when in the Pulpit.
- John Haller, a Sailor, by Falling from the Top of the Rigging of the *Mary*, on to the Deck and Dashed to Pieces.
- Solomon Harris, from his falling into the Fire, when Lighting his Pipe for a Smoke, and was Burnt to Death.
- Miss Hopkins, from her Dress taking Fire, and Seriously Burning her.
- Colonel John and others, Thrown from the Chaise, on the Richmond Road.

- A Keeper, Bitten by a Brazilian Weasel, in the Zoological Gardens.
- The Duchess of Kent, by Collision near Holland Road.
- Lieut. Love, by Playing with a Scithe, with which he Cut his Thigh and Bled to Death.
- Miss M'Clure, Bitten by a Mad Dog in Salford, which Caused her Death, from Hydrophobia.
- The Manchester Coach, Laden with Convicts Upset near Birmingham, and the Convicts escaped.
- At Manchester, from an Omnibus on Trial, Breaking down and Killing one Man and Seriously injuring two others.
- Granville Pigot, Shot by his own Gun, near Stowe.
- General Weatherall, Thrown from his Gig by Collision with a Runaway Gig and Thrown Seriously Out.
- Mr Wright, of Red Lion Hill, Hampstead, his little Son Shot by another Boy.
- The Yorkshire Coach Upset at Westbrook, and two Females and a Man Seriously Wounded.
- Stephen Karkelt, Buried Alive in Newlyn Mine, under four Ton of Rubbish that had Fallen on him.

Such variety in everyday disaster was diminished in the next century, when the Reaper's scythe was sparked sharper by the mass-production machinery of the automobile industry.

### The Curse of Jehu

There are over 400 million motor vehicles in the world, joined by 50 million new ones every year. They kill 4,655 Britons annually, and 47,000 Americans – more than were killed in Vietnam. There are 9.7 road deaths a year for each 100,000 of the British population, 18.3 for the USA, 20.5 in France and, the worst, 31.5 in Portugal. The British kill yearly 1,261 car drivers, 481 on motorbikes and 242 on bicycles, but no bus drivers, and they run over 1,496 pedestrians, most of them over seventy.

Unlike most melancholy statistics, which unflinchingly mount, these are hearteningly falling. British fatalities are now the lowest since records began in 1926, the days of the green open Bentley and T-model Ford, when you wrapped up cosily in a tartan rug, drew on your gauntlets, munched Rowntree's Motoring Chocolate and never counted your drinks on a spin to the roadhouse.

This improvement blatantly derives from the better design of cars and roads, but partly from advances in the techniques of surgery and resuscitation, and in the control of infection, which similarly reduced the deaths from wounds in the US Army by a third between the two World Wars. But the 4,655 British deaths could be further reduced to 745, because 84 per cent of them were caused by human error.

Drivers were mostly going too fast, not giving way, overtaking imprudently, following too close, and thinking about something else at the time. Such lapses arise from the change of personality which is inflicted by driving as markedly as by drugs.

'Woman reduces us all to the common denominator,' wrote George Bernard Shaw. So does the motor car. Whatever our intellectual, social, monetary or sexual status, once behind the wheel we are as one. Ford was a more effective mechanic of Communism than Lenin.

The car gives power to the downtrodden, sexual expression to the frustrated, indignant admonition to the nonentity, a symbol of honour to the dishonourable, a weapon to the aggressive, a cockade to the vain, an excuse to the impatient, a temptation to the impulsive, anonymity to the irresponsible, and fantasies to the mass of men who lead lives of quiet desperation. These visions are brilliantly sharpened by the motor manufacturers – all as lethally unscrupulous as the cigarette makers – who invest their products with Grand Prix performance in

**180**

speed, road-holding, tastefulness, prestige and seductiveness.

The car extends the cosy security of home; it is the cherished possession, the glittering projection of the family, to be cleaned regularly with an assiduousness which, applied to the teeth, would leave the dental profession half-idle. It becomes furnished with little square satin cushions and coat hangers, decorated with protective religious ornaments and dangling teddy bears, and plastered with expressions of the owner's beliefs and opinions. The discarding of its L-plates is for the male a rite of passage exultantly proclaiming initiation into maturity, and it is second to the bed as the favoured site of sexual intercourse.

Eighty per cent of men have driving licences, but under fifty per cent of women, who use cars to get the children to school and the shopping from the supermarket, not as metallic materialisations of their fantasies. Yet women suffer the unthinking disparagement of their driving which Victorian men applied to female intellects.

Though eight hundred Britons a year killed on the roads have been drinking, it is not a modern problem: 'Accidents are not miraculous events, when men live hard, and drive after dinner,' noticed Ralph Nickleby in 1838.

Nor is speed: 'They ought to be prosecuted and fined, them Mails. They come racing out of Lad Lane and Wood Street at twelve or fourteen mile an hour, them Mails do. The only wonder is, that people ain't killed oftener by the Mails,' grumbled an onlooker to an accident in *Little Dorrit*.

It is unwise to avoid injury and death by staying at home. That is where most accidents happen. Over 500 children are killed in their homes every year, by choking, suffocating, scalding, burning, falling, or poisoning themselves with their parents' drugs. The adult who passes a peaceful average of sixteen hours a day at home, over two uneventful years, has faced the same risk of injury as if he were driving a motorbike continually for 350 hours. It is safer to travel hopefully than to arrive.


### War and Peace

'It is a sweet and seemly thing to die for one's country,' said Horace. But few poets or philosophers since have thought coolly why so drastic a necessity should so regularly arise.

From Brest to Hamburg, from Calais to Basle, stretches a cemetery of infinite sadness, a memorial to the busiest of the Reaper's activities, incited by one set of humans against an almost indistinguishable other.

The causes of wars are uncountable; the cause of war is perplexing. Freud's death instinct, thanatos, has been invoked by psychologists who accept that we are all unconsciously bent on self-destruction. This explanation was paraded in disguise by Bertrand Russell, who wrote resignedly:

> Yet, if there is nothing further, an ethical disagreement can only be decided by emotional appeals, or by force – in the ultimate resort, by war. On questions of fact, we can appeal to science and scientific methods of observation: but on ultimate questions of ethics there seems to be nothing analogous.

Or war may equally reasonably break out from an exuberance of our opposing instinct, that of self-preservation.

And war sings to the young, the bored and the unfulfilled a deadly siren's song.

President Hoover recognised that 'Older men declare war. But it is youth that must fight and die.' Bernard

Shaw was more specific about 'the bad blood of the fierce little cowards at home who egg on others to fight for the gratification of their national vanity!' But Professor Hans Zinsser of Columbia University, who wrote *Rats, Lice and History* about bubonic plague and typhus (more devastating afflictions of mankind than war), reflected about America in 1917:

> Think of the man who has lived meagerly in a frame house on the outskirts of Somerville or Weehawken, and for ten years – except for two weeks in August – has regularly caught the eight-fifteen, spent the rest of the day floorwalking, and then caught the six-twenty back to what he came from in the morning! Think of his feelings of release and self-satisfaction when he is marching up Broadway behind the band, between files of cheering garment workers. Think of his pride in a renewed manhood, standing guard at dawn or lying behind a pile of sandbags pot-shooting his fellow man, or drinking beer with his comrades – knowing that the world approves him as a hero, and that his family has the government to look out for it forever and ever!
>
> But beyond the release from boredom there is the joy in uniforms which stimulates war. The instinct for fancy dress is hard to kill, as anybody knows who has been in a town where the Mystic Knights or the Shriners or the Red Indians were holding a convention: or even in Boston, when the Ancient and Honourables are blocking traffic on Beacon Hill. And, further, there is the applause of the women, – not women in general, but each man's own women, – who, as instinctively as the men like to play soldiers, have the hereditary longing to glorify the brave brutalities that their heroes write home about . . .

Luckily, floorwalkers – whether they like it or not – have had no recent occasion to march behind the band up Broadway, Whitehall, the Champs-Elysées or Unter den Linden. Heroic nationalistic war, the world's traditional means of competition, has become outdated by the world's generous self-provisioning with atomic weapons.

> Then it may well be that we shall by a process of sublime irony have reached a stage in this story where safety will be the sturdy child of terror, and survival the twin brother of annihilation

declared Sir Winston Churchill in the House of Commons on 1 May 1955, displaying how much more philosophical he was than Bertrand Russell, who so objected to atomic bombs that he frequently sat on pavements to prove it.

# THIRTEEN

# The Future of Mankind

Standing firmly on the commonsensical plank that we cannot see into the future – because it has not yet happened – let us scan the heavens for humanity's persevering attempts to do so.

## What Your Stars Foretell

The showy phenomena overhead, day and night, understandably terrified man since the time he evolved sufficiently from the apes to start thinking about them. In addition to the heavenly bodies clearly tormenting him with tempest, aridity and flood, they were suspected of mysterious direct effects on his brutish and short existence.

Since the fifteenth century, science has been busily abating this celestial menace by measuring and sorting out the universe. Science is not over-concerned where the universe is, and what goes on outside it: the immeasurable is unthinkable. As we were reminded by the Autocrat of the Breakfast-Table, man has difficulty in grasping a schedule more imaginative than the cosmic extension of a railway timetable.

Though astronomers' telescopes began purposefully to

prod the sky during the lives of Galileo and Newton, the established astrologers continued to be cherished by the rulers of Europe as their public relations persons are today.

Astrology was first codified by the Babylonians in the sixth century BC; it appealed to the Greeks, who three centuries later brought it to the Egyptians. Astrology engineered the sun, the moon and the planets Jupiter, Venus, Saturn, Mercury and Mars into celestial machinery whose movements shone with significance to the stargazing priests. Astrologers reasoned that if something had happened when these spheres stood in a particular relationship, then it might happen again when they did so next. No one had a shining example of this. But there were always crops that burgeoned or failed, herds that thrived or died, and battles that were won or lost, which could be laid in retrospect at the heavenly door.

The effect of this starry influence on humanity, for better or worse, mysteriously continues in popularity. The ancients' Zodiac is depicted in every morning's newspapers. This was a band of twelve constellations, radiating their influence upon earth for successive months:

- Aries the Ram
- Taurus the Bull
- Gemini the Twins
- Cancer the Crab
- Leo the Lion
- Virgo the Virgin
- Libra the Scales
- Scorpio the Scorpion
- Sagittarius the Archer
- Capricorn the Goat
- Aquarius the Water-carrier
- Pisces the Fish

**186**

Their positions in the sky at your birth, as observed by the astrological sextant, set your course through life. The *Titanic* was sunk only incidentally by the iceberg. The ship was doomed through her captain being born when Neptune was in the House of Death. Worse, on that disastrous night in the Atlantic, Uranus (the catastrophe constellation) was in opposition to where the moon had found itself on the captain's birthday. It would have signalled to any prudent skipper to drop anchor in Southampton Water.

If Napoleon at Waterloo had added up the letters of his name, plus his birthday and the day's date, then performed the same calculation for Wellington, he would have seen plainly that the morning of 18 June 1815 was for him one when all conflict must be avoided. But for Wellington, it was to be a day of decisive action and immediate attainment. Had the Emperor mastered his stars as he had his strategy, European history would have been given a different date to remember and a different course to follow.

Newspaper horoscopes, like the football pools forecasts, are presumably read intently but cynically by their beneficiaries. One of Britain's cultured Sunday papers assured me in its latest magazine that: 'Powerful aspects next week signify changes in your lifestyle.' I waited restlessly: the lifestyle of an ageing author is insufferably dull, peering through half-moons at a word-processor screen all morning, taking out the dog in the afternoon, then a seemly Scotch, a domestic dinner, a book and bedtime. I dreamt of an upheaval of Hemingway voluptuousness. Nothing happened, though the dog had to go to the vet.

As some half a million people are born every day, and they are all different, the star-spangled baby's bonnet must sometimes fit. But humanity would be less often disappointed if we comfortably accepted the stars as the

187

places where the angels have put their feet through the sky.

On Saturday, 15 September 1934, the *Daily Express* asked, 'Is it your Birthday?'

Yes, it was my thirteenth.

The horoscope beneath told me: 'You have a contemplative, analytical mind, a fluent pen. Sure success awaits you as a writer, particularly as a critic.'

Flattering. But damned odd.

### Soothsayers

Michel de Notredame was born in 1503 at St-Rémy-de-Provence, south of Avignon. The little town became famous through the painting of Vincent van Gogh, who in 1890 spent some time in the local asylum before he shot himself.

De Notredame graduated in 1529 from the medical centre of excellence at Montpellier, about the same time as the renownedly argumentative Swiss physician Theophrastus Bombastus von Hohenheim, self-named 'Paracelsus'. Montpellier was strong on the practice of prognosis. This is the medical skill of forecasting the course of any disease. The technique was established by Hippocrates, from observation of the patient's pose in bed, his breathing, his spit, his urine, his face. 'Nose sharp, eyes hollow, temples shrunken, ears cold and with their lobes turned outward, the skin of the face parched and tense, the colour yellow or very dusky' reliably signalled impending death.

Dr de Notredame practised in Salon-de-Provence, a bigger town on the way to Marseilles. There he extended his prognostic skills, by turning from the slop-bucket to the stars. In 1555, he published as 'Nostradamus' his first volume of *Centuries*, which were rhymed prophecies taking us to happenings in the year 3797, after which no more were necessary, as it would be the world's last.

*Centuries* made such an impact on the reading classes that the following year the Queen, Catherine de' Medici, who was tryingly superstitious, summoned Nostradamus to Court at St-Germain-en-Laye and commanded him to cast her nine children's horoscopes. In 1559, Catherine's husband Henri II died of an accidental wound behind the eye inflicted through his visor by the Captain of his Scottish Guard during a tournament. Nostradamus was seen to have foretold this in his quatrain:

> The young lion will overcome the old
> On the battlefield in single combat:
> He will put out his eyes within a cage of gold:
> Two wounds in one, then death, cruel death.

The verse notably expresses the valuable vagueness of all twelve volumes of Nostradamus' prophesies.

> Nine years the thin one held sway in peace,
> Then he developed a thirst for blood:
> For him, a great people without face and without law
> will die,
> Killed by one much more easygoing.

This one has been applied to Hitler and Franklin D. Roosevelt in 1942. Trim-waisted vegetarian Hitler came to power in 1933, and FDR had a genial way on his radio chats. Nothing about the moustache and the cigarette-holder, though.

Nostradamus admitted readily to deliberately veiling his illuminations of the future. He needed to take care to avoid offending the Church or the King and thereby invoking disaster upon himself in this world, or offending God and thereby storing it up in the next. Perhaps his collection of *Centuries* was a rambling hoax, to incite the

**189**

serious unravelling by his contemporary intellectuals, for whose ignorance he enjoyed a profitable contempt.

Outside his front door in the evening sunshine of Salon, Nostradamus was once greeted by his neighbour's pretty young daughter, tripping to gather the kindling in the woods.

'Bonjour, Monsieur de Notredame,' she said, smiling at him.

'Bonjour, fillette,' he replied amiably.

She was away an hour.

'Bonjour, Monsieur de Notredame,' she repeated cheerily.

'Bonjour, petite femme,' he congratulated her.

If the future is readily predictable, then predict it.

Nostradamus' fellow student Paracelsus became a wandering physician; vain, arrogant, iconoclastic, but practical and scientific, his renown spread uneasily across Europe. 'I pleased no one except the sick whom I healed,' he claimed proudly. Paracelsus thundered that the temple of healing stood upon four pillars: philosophy, virtue, alchemy and astrology. But his notion of astrology was predictably original. He accepted that the stars influenced humanity, but as he believed the stars could do as they pleased, so could man.

Paracelsus died in 1541. Nostradamus, who suffered severely from gout, died in 1566, leaving six children. His tomb in Salon was visited by Louis XIII and Louis XIV, and during the Revolution the Gardes Nationales scattered his bones and drank wine from his skull. His reassembled skeleton now lies behind the wall of Saint Laurient's church on the road to Avignon. Both soothsayers might have chidingly foretold the remark of Scottish physician Sir James Mackenzie, who died in 1925: 'No doctor lives long enough to write a reliable book on prognosis.'

When Queen Catherine's second son became King

Charles IX of France, he had wanted to kill off Nostradamus, and cordially invited the soothsayer to foretell the hour of his death. Nostradamus replied: 'Sire, the fates have withheld from me the exact hour of my death, but, on consulting the stars, I found out this much, that I shall die some very short time before your Majesty.' Nostradamus was made Court physician instead.

This story was expectedly applied to other astrologers. Early in 1708, Swift wrote *Predictions for the Ensuing Year, by Isaac Bickerstaff*, foreseeing the death on the following 29 March of the fashionable English astrologer, ex-cobbler John Partridge. On 30 March, Swift published a letter describing this sad event. Partridge protested furiously that he was still alive. Swift wrote a *Vindication*, proving that he was certainly dead. Partridge was unable to foresee jokes.

In 1627, 25-year-old William Lilly from Leicestershire, for seven years an old man's servant in London, married his master's wealthy and younger widow. She had earlier married two other elderly husbands. Five years later, she herself died and left Lilly £1,000, which enabled him to embrace astrology, from which he became famous and richer.

Lilly issued the yearly *Merlinus Anglicus, Junior*, which anticipated Dr Francis Moore's *Old Moore's Almanac* of 1700 (this was originally titled *Vox Stellarum*, but predicted only the weather and promoted Dr Moore's patent Lambeth pills). Lilly enjoyed the grave attention of leading MPs in the Long Parliament, garnering their gossip to fortify his astrological predictions. He joined the Cromwellians in the Civil War once he foresaw that they would win, found himself unpopular after the Restoration, and in 1666 claimed to have foretold in 1651 the Great Fire of London. The prediction did him no good, as he was then arrested for having caused it.

Top American astrologer Evangeline Adams arrived for

the first time in New York at the start of this century, announced at the reception desk that her hotel was under planetary 'conditions terrifying in their unfriendliness', and escaped when it satisfactorily burnt to the ground that night. Ludwig von Wohl came to London from Germany in 1935, and helped the war effort by supplying the British government with the astrological advice certainly being impressed on the top Nazis. Hitler had many oddities, but was not star-struck. His deputy, Rudolf Hess, employed several astrologers, all of whom were arrested by a fellow Zodiac enthusiast, Himmler, who ran the Gestapo, after Hess's embarrassing starlight flight by Messerschmitt to Scotland in 1941.

The future can be seen with less brainwork, if more mess, by opening up a slaughtered animal and rummaging among its entrails.

'What say the augurers?' asked Julius Caesar, early on that murderous morning in the Senate.

His servant told him gloomily:

> They would not have you to stir forth today.
> Plucking the entrails of an offering forth,
> They could not find a heart within the beast.

Less startling than this anatomical portent are those of hepatoscopy, another favourite of the Babylonians and Greeks. The liver was thought to be the soul's fountain, because it was bursting with the blood which mysteriously flowed through the body, and so represented life. As sacrificed animals assumed the character of the god to whom they were offered, inspection of their livers gave the knowing priests insight into that god's mind. They asked the god, as they stuck the knife into the squealing sheep, whether the coming harvest or war would turn out agreeably. They had his answer immediately from handling the warm, gory, dripping liver and turning over their book of omens.

The sheep's liver, like the human's, has a big and a small lobe, a gall bladder with its ducts, many arteries and veins, and presents a gleaming surface. Tiny variations of all these indicated to the sacrificers important coming changes. A long duct to the gall bladder bestowed a long reign on the king; a swollen gall bladder meant the extension of his dominions, or that the poor beast had suffered from cholecystitis.

On the basic astrological principle, if a liver looked as another liver did when something had last happened, then it was a reasonable bet that it would happen again. If it did, it afforded the soothsayers agreeable and useful respect and authority. If it did not, people forgot. Hepatoscopy has recently returned to fashion, with inspection of the human liver through a small hole in the abdomen by a laparoscope, and if its findings are less sweeping they are more reliable.

The most convenient soothsaying lies in the palm of the hand. The fleshy bumps have been aggrandised by palmists to 'mounts', their size indicating what proportion the rest of you contains of the qualities assigned to each one. The Mount of Jupiter at the base of the index finger expresses your ambition and pride (if too big, you are conceited). Below the middle finger arises the Mount of Saturn, the gauge of prudence and wisdom, which by a millimetre or two's diminution can turn you from one who is sober, wise and successful into an ignorant failure. The Mount of Venus at the ball of the thumb can with equally frightening slightness expand your sex life from respectable loving to delightful lechery.

Even the bumps on your fingers have an importance beyond that prized by the police: the three on the little finger alone indicate your goodness, prudence and reflectiveness. The lines running across the palm – the line of life round the ball of the thumb, the line of heart below the fingers and the line of head under it – by their variations and relations reveal your mixture of all the qualities that humans possess, and predict where these will land you. Large hands show a grasp of detail, clenched ones dynamism, and gracefully swooping ones reveal that you are popular at parties (they are also the sign of an affectionate nature).

Anatomists view the palm with equal fascination. Lying deep in our hand is a tough fibrous sheet that prevents the hand's tendons, which run from our forearm muscles to our fingertips, forming long ridges whenever we grasp anything. Otherwise, we should drop it. This strong fascia can become diseased and shrink, giving the famous Dupuytren's contracture. The fascia sends off fibrous bands to the surface, which make lines in the palmar skin. The form of these lines is ordained by the different shapes of our hand's bones and tendons, not by our fate. Their furrows emphasise the normal subcutaneous fat, which pouts between them, and there are your mounts. The Mount of Venus is created by the muscles of the thumb, which like other muscles can be enlarged by exercise, so buy a hand-developer and make yourself more amorous.

Though these anatomical arrangements provide us with a firm grip rather than a glimpse into our character or future, frail humans still pay eagerly to display their hands before women on seaside piers and in fairground tents and gypsy caravans, as they did to the earliest predecessors of these handy charlatans five thousand years ago in China. Moleosophy is a variation revealing such things from our moles. Round moles indicate goodness, black moles a dark future, moles on the buttocks announce lack of ambition, on the groin lack of money, on the hip contentment, on a woman's navel sexiness, on her nipple social pushiness. This psychic investigation is best performed between friends.

Soothsayers tired of holding unwashed fingers can buy a crystal ball, the contemplation of which is of ancient usage and dignified as 'scrying'. Flitting images in its depths may be the gazer's own memories and ideas, made visual through autohypnosis, which can be induced by gazing fixedly at a light, or a bright pendulum, or anything glittering. More likely, the scryer is seeing nothing more revealing than her own reflection.

Even simpler is reading the future from tea-leaves. This is best done on a winter afternoon by the fire, with a broad, white cup of steaming Darjeeling, and sensibly a dish of hot buttered crumpets. Drink the tea; then, holding the handle in the left hand, swirl the slops three times from left to right, plastering the leaves round the cup sides. Events indicated at the rim are imminent, those on the bottom far distant. The tea-leaves form symbols: e.g., an angel means good news, an axe danger, a crown indicates impending honours, a ring a coming marriage, a snake a lurking enemy. As these shapes can be imaginatively visualised from any scattering whatever, it is best to decide first what fortune you wish to enjoy before you can pour yourself a second cup.

After tea, draw the curtains, arrange the lamp, and tell your future from dealing a pack of cards. Every one of them has its significance. The king of spades portends danger to your marriage or to your business, his queen warns of a cruel and treacherous acquaintance, the jack, or knave, of a parasitic friend, the ace of spades famously heralds death. Try to turn up clubs, whose court promises instead generous companions, lovable women, sincere cronies, and – through the ace – wealth, fame and popularity.

Easier still is rolling dice, which answer such questions as:

'Does the one I love love me?'

A pair of ones say, 'Only if you are sincere'; a double six says, 'Yes, but look out, your lover's susceptible.'

'Shall I ever be rich?'

Respectively, 'Not while you long to be'; and 'Yes, but it won't do you any good.'

Divination of the future by dice is not an offshoot of American crap games; the Greeks were doing it in the temple of Heracles in Achaea, and the Chinese in 600 BC.

No comment on this ingrained hopefulness of mankind betters *Extraordinary Popular Delusions* in 1841:

> How flattering to the pride of man to think that the stars in their courses watch over him, and typify, by their movements and aspects, the joys or the sorrows that await him! He, less in proportion to the universe than the all-but invisible insects that feed in myriads on a summer's leaf are to this great globe itself, fondly imagines that eternal worlds were chiefly created to prognosticate his fate. How we should pity the arrogance of the worm that crawls at our feet, if we knew that it also desired to know the secrets of futurity, and imagined that meteors shot athwart the sky to warn it that a tom-tit was hovering near to gobble it up; that storms and earthquakes, the revolutions of empires, or the fall of mighty monarchs, only happened to predict its birth, its progress, and its decay! Not a whit less presuming has man shewn himself; not a whit less arrogant are the sciences, so called, of astrology, augury, necromancy, geomancy, palmistry, and divination of every kind.

The *British Medical Journal* in 1993 published a paper from the Medical Research Council, which studied the finger and palm prints of 139 men and women born in Lancashire during the period 1935–43 and still living there. Those whose fingerprints had more whorl patterns than patterns of loops or arches had been recorded as thin at birth, and now suffered a higher blood pressure than the rest. The more whorl-patterned fingers they had, particularly on the right hand, the higher was their blood pressure. The same affliction struck those with long and narrow hands. The effect was created in the womb during the development of the finger pads, at the stage between thirteen and nineteen weeks of pregnancy, when critical changes were occurring in the development of the baby's arteries.

'Fingertip whorls and a narrow palmar angle are indelible markers of impaired fetal development at different stages in pregnancy,' the Medical Research Council concluded.

If our palm can indicate so definitely one effect of our development in the womb, why not some of the others that make us into what we are?

Fascinating. But damned odd.

FOURTEEN

# The Spirit is Willing

In 1847, the tenant of a small, square clapboard house at Hydesville, in Wayne County of upstate New York, moved out because of mysterious knocks on the door at night. Coming in was the methodist John D. Fox and his family, which embraced two pretty, dark-haired daughters, Margaret, aged fifteen and Katie, twelve. Moving house had the effect on the girls' lives of Cinderella's lost slipper.

### Heavenly Voices

The knocking and thumping in the wooden house increased to a nightly racket at the sisters' bedtime. The bedroom floor started shaking; the furniture and bedroom bits and pieces were falling about. On the disturbed Friday night of 31 March 1848, the sisters counter-attacked. They snapped their fingers and clapped their hands, inviting the nuisance: 'Mr Splitfoot, do as I do!' To which he instantly responded, his rap for their clap.

A code was quickly struck: raps for each letter of the alphabet, and for 'yes' and 'no'. The sisters shortly realised that they were talking to Mr Charles Haynes, who was murdered by the now departed neighbours five years earlier, and whose corpse was in the cellar. They went down to dig him up. They found only a handful of hair and some bones, though among these Mrs Fox recognised confidently a piece of human skull.

In three weeks, the Fox family were locally famous, though sniffily excluded from their methodist church. They moved west to the girls' older, married sister, Mrs Leah Fish of Rochester, on the south shore of Lake Ontario. Leah had the notion of exploiting her sisters as a spiritual public telegraph office between the living and dead of Rochester. This quickly spread their reputation across neighbouring states. Margaret and Katie went on tour, made several thousand dollars, swept into society and originated the vocation of medium.

Margaret and Katie were not the first interpreters of spiritual rappings. We have already met twelve-year-old Miss Parsons of Cock Lane in London, to whom the coded knocks for 'yes' and 'no' from Miss Fanny, lying unsuspectedly in her Clerkenwell grave, imparted that she had been murdered. The London public paid eagerly to see the supernatural child; later her father was pilloried and her mother jailed for conniving with her deception.

A couple of years after the Fox girls' debut, America was mad on 'spiritualism'. England preferred to call it 'spiritism' or 'spirit-rapping', to distinguish it from the spiritual view of things taken by philosophers. In 1860, Dickens's new weekly *All the Year Round* was defining: 'Witchcraft, demonology, possession, and the like, revived in the modest phrase of Spiritualism'.

The first International Spiritualist Congress was held in Cleveland, Ohio, in 1852. Europe sent delegates, but in spirit. The spiritualists dispatched a petition to Congress: 'The undersigned, citizens of the Republic of the United States' – 14,000 of them – 'respectfully ask to exhibit to your honours certain physical and intellectual

**199**

phenomena of mysterious origin and tendency, which have manifested themselves recently in this country . . .'

That year, there were fifty practising mediums in England, who were invited to tea-parties. A famous one was Daniel Douglas Home, born in 1833 in Edinburgh, a relation of the Earl of Home, ancestor of a prime minister. At seventeen, Daniel had become a top American medium, who impressed the poet William Cullen Bryant and in 1852 floated in the air. This quality he employed in 1868 to float out of one window and return through another, in the presence of two members of the Scottish aristocracy.

After returning to England, Daniel Home had the Brownings to his performances, became a Catholic, went to Rome, held seances before the crowned heads of Europe, but was expelled in 1864 as a sorcerer. He then became the adopted son of a Mrs Lyon for £60,000, but she got her money back, and he died in France aged fifty-three.

There were then two hundred mediums in Germany, but France went in for table-turning. Half a dozen men and women sat, with intense expressions, hand-touching on the table in the salon, until it inevitably and wishfully moved. These parties provided the caricaturist Daumier richly with material. There were accompanying spiritual knockings, which spoilsports attributed to cracking knee joints and feet.

The French *séance* evolved the *planchette* and the ouija board. These were platforms on wheels pierced with a pencil, by which the medium's hand could produce heavenly messages. They varied from cookery hints to dispatches from Joan of Arc and Napoleon, enlivened by some obscene ethereal calls, ascribed to evil spirits.

Spiritualism became a cult, with the cosy, introverted, self-sustaining faith of any other. I have tediously quoted the misbelief that if everyone you meet believes the same thing, then it must be true. The believers in spiritualism were mostly middle-aged women, who sang a hymn, listened respectfully to the medium describing the here-after, and sat suggestibly in the dim light to hear their dead loved ones address them, though their reported conversation appears as banal as doubtless it was during life.

Some mediums brandished floating trumpets; some sprouted flowers; some exuded 'ectoplasm' – this could be gas, or liquid or solid – which was luminous and was released from the mediums' bodily orifices. In photographs, it resembles exuberant bubble-gum. Some had themselves roped down; some rose in the air; some spoke unexpectedly in foreign languages. Some extended their functions beyond seeing into the future or expressing the opinions of the deceased, and began healing the sick, guided by dead doctors. A quarter of a million Britons still spend their Sunday evenings at spiritualist meetings, and there are 500 mediums in New York, many controlled by spirituous Red Indians.

Conjuring is simple, and trick photography simpler, as illustrated by the UFOs. So seems spiritualism. In 1888, forty years after their smash success, its founding sisters Margaret and Katie Fox told the *New York Herald*:

> Spiritualism is deception, from beginning to end. It's the greatest deception of the century! Our sister Leah was 22 years older than us . . . It was she who pushed us into deceiving the public!

There is much money to be made from uncritical widows.

## Soulmates

The Roman Catholic Church is against spiritualism. Since 24 April 1917 its flock is not permitted 'to watch any spiritualist manifestation, even presented with honesty and piety'. The Church of England is more easygoing, though noting charitably that many spiritual communications fall below the 'mental capacity shown by the communicant while they were still alive'.

Spiritualism presumes spirits, but humanity suffers an undying confusion about its soul. Is the soul some undetectable substance imprisoned within us, released on death to exist for ever (whatever 'for ever' is)? Is it a complex of everything we know, feel and want? Is it the final fading grin on the face of the Cheshire Cat? Or is it only the difference between a car with its engine running and with the engine switched off?

'Said Descartes, I extol myself, because I have a soul and beasts do not. Of course, he had to put Descartes before the horse,' once jollied *The Times*.

If our dogs shall never lift their legs against the Pearly Gates, at some moment in man's ascent from animals via the apes God must have tapped man's hairy shoulder and congratulated him on having achieved a soul. Life for man would henceforth be succeeded by something more enjoyable among the angels, if he became a Christian or Muhammadan; or at least followed by something different, through turning into somebody else, or into a cow or a lily, were he a Buddhist. Such distinctions are unimportant. The simple notion of life after death expresses an enviable optimism that, applied to the time before that unfortunate event, would make our world a place of delightful cheeriness.

But if we *do* become angels, why should we manifest ourselves only through those weird, dubious, exploiting persons who declare themselves to be mediums?

## Every Day's a Doomsday

The foreseeing spirit, speaking while still imprisoned in the human frame, is generally depressing.

That the end of the world is nigh need not be assiduously proclaimed by seedy, gloomy men with placards and leaflets, standing in the rain on street corners. It is in every morning's papers. Predicting the future by the facts seems consistently more doomful than doing so by the fates.

> In 1951 the Conservative Party had promised a Britain strong and free. Now Britain's strength, freedom and solvency apparently depend on the proceeds of a squalid raffle . . . There are hundreds and thousands of people in Britain who will be outraged by this proposal, and I suggest that the Chancellor remove it from his financial planning,

demanded the future Labour Prime Minister, Harold Wilson, of present Conservative Chancellor of the Exchequer Harold Macmillan in the House of Commons, immediately after Budget Day in 1956.

The doom to Britain's strength, freedom and solvency in 1956 was the Premium Bond, which bore no interest but awarded infrequent and modest prizes through Ernie, a number machine basking near Blackpool. The only demoralisation inflicted over some forty years is resentment among the bigger winners at the steady reduction of income tax, since the prizes come tax-free.

Two years earlier, the former Labour Deputy Prime Minister, Herbert Morrison, had enlightened the House about another prized Conservative Government proposal:

> . . . the scheme was going to help monopoly and was a Tory plot on behalf of big business against the little man. If a general election occurred before the

proposals were properly working, it would be simple to scrap them entirely and produce a more workable system, but if the scheme should be in operation 'when we take office' Labour would maintain and enforce the full rigour of the safeguards in the Bill and others which might be put in, and they could not guarantee compensation for the loss which programme contractors would suffer if they were put out of business.

In the Upper House, even Conservative Lord Halifax needed to admit that 'the Government's modifications did not hide the disagreeable realities of the Bill'. And Earl De La Warr, who was charged with putting the disgraceful measure through the Lords, admitted with a pained jumble of humility and honour that:

> The Government had tried hard to recognise the strength of feeling and depth of sincerity which had existed on both sides, and had tried to meet every reasonable fear, including fears which the Government did not share, because they believed in the dignity and traditions of British trade and commerce.

In 1954, the country had bleakly looked into the abyss on the screens of commercial television. This brash rival to the worthy, non-profit-seeking, advertisement-uncontaminated BBC became lawful, following such an apocalyptic welcome, only after its shackling with the precautions that:

> . . . the programmes were to be of high quality, and nothing was to be included which offended against good taste or decency or which was likely to encourage or incite to crime or to lead to disorder or to be offensive to public feeling.

Attempts to prohibit advertisements on Sunday, Christmas Day and Good Friday failed, as did the banning of commercials for drink, but the Government guaranteed that ads would never interrupt religious services nor any programmes presenting the Queen.

Such self-important sanctimoniousness was echoed in churches and halls throughout the country, and the Government needed the Parliamentary guillotine to push the Bill through a head-shaking House. Reality was shortly re-established by an early programme contractor admitting jovially: 'It's just like having a licence to print your own money.'

To elected representatives, the future ends at the next election. Predictions until then must be tokens of electoral wooing. In 1968, Enoch Powell MP quoted Virgil to Birmingham about immigration:

> As I look ahead, I am filled with foreboding. Like the Roman, I seem to see 'the River Tiber foaming with much blood'.

It is a tribute to national character that such waters remain unalarmingly muddied.

The grimmest menace to mankind is currently the environment. The term was defined by Einstein as 'everything that is not me'. Thus it offers a wide target for the slings and arrows of outrageous misfortune.

Since 1984, the world has spasmodically trembled about the holes in the ozone widening over its poles as steadily as split rubber and threatening skin cancers and cataracts. It has also become alarmed about the warming of the world's atmosphere, which will melt the polar ice and put Brighton and Atlantic City under water. In 1989, two hundred scientists of the American space agency NASA, just back from six weeks at Stavanger in Norway, announced with decisive doomfulness that the Arctic atmosphere was 'primed for ozone destruction'.

To prevent these disasters, man sprays his armpits, his

**205**

woodwork and his wasps with CFC-free aerosols, and fills the family car up with lead-free petrol. Such altruism provides a pleasant feeling of righteousness. God having gone out of fashion, and man needing to believe in *something*, he follows the environmental saints and their zealous priests and goes green, in varying shades of intensity. He religiously carries his uplifting beliefs to the crematorium, which will deal with him at 850 degrees instead of 650, to comply with the 1990 Environmental Protection Act, which controls the noxious gases that he finally heretically gives off.

In 1993, another lot of scientists in Britain found that, despite an 18 per cent depletion of the ozone overhead, solar radiation had fallen, thanks to the protective clouds of pollution.

In 1986, the World Health Organisation was authoritatively predicting that 100 million people worldwide would have Aids by 1990. The Royal College of Nursing knowledgeably put it at a million cases in Britain, which works out at one in fifty of the population. In 1993, Aids cases in Britain were levelling off at 6,929 a year, including about 1,000 homosexuals and only 63 heterosexuals. This is a fifth of the Government's gloomiest prognosis, and half of its most optimistic. Each year Aids treatment and prevention claims £200 million, and – truly doomfully – 800 lives. But one necessity of the 1980s has easefully vanished: impatience to have lots of sex while it is still safe.

In those queasy years, 'mad cow disease' terrified gourmets away from *tête de veau* and *cervelle au beurre noir*, and implanted in the public a nightmare of its shortly mooing and stomping about in lunatic herds. The Creutzfeldt-Jakob virus in cattle brain can spread to man, causing presenile dementia and epilepsy, but rarely. In 1991, the disease unhappily claimed 32 patients in Britain. In 1993, it was 48 – a rise statistically insignificant. Its experts nevertheless now recommend epicures also to avoid common *boudin* and black pudding as well.

The dropping of the H-bomb is a prospective doom which everyone has grown shruggingly used to, like death itself. To make sure we know that it will be even worse than expected, the British Medical Association in 1988 issued helpful directions on the *Selection of Casualties for Treatment after Nuclear Attack.*

It will be premature after the atomic blast to congratulate ourselves as wounded but still alive, because 'We see no categorical solution to the problem of mercy killing of survivors who would otherwise experience great suffering followed by certain death,' the BMA confessed. The vexation for the doctors would be deciding who to kill. Injured children would be a trying liability, because as many children as possible need to enjoy the limited care, instead of being left to die, to avoid raising the ire of the surviving adults.

The elderly would stand a laughable chance of treatment, and it would be clearly silly to allow the survival of sufferers with chronic illnesses, such as diabetes or epilepsy, because the drugs for their future care would have vanished in a nuclear-shattered world. Nor would anyone smitten with atomic radiation require attention, because they would shortly perish anyway. Workers skilled to maintain the basic services would enjoy priority. 'The plumber, the carpenter and the stone mason will have much more to offer after the bomb than the business executive, the Civil Servant, and even, in some cases, the doctor,' the BMA recognised sensibly.

Six million people in Britain would be seriously injured by the bomb, but another twenty-eight million – half the population – would relieve the doctors' ethical difficulties by being killed instantly. Doctors and nurses are warned by the BMA to keep clear of the injured languishing in areas of nuclear contamination, for fear of contaminating themselves.

Michelangelo could have made something of it all for the ceiling of the United Nations Assembly.

In the spring of 1913, James Thurber was aged eighteen in Columbus, Ohio, when the dam broke.

The population of Columbus streamed into the streets in wild panic, screaming, 'Go east! Go east!' The dread news had come when someone in the High Street began to run – perhaps he was late to meet his wife – to be joined by a newsboy in high spirits, then by a portly gentleman of affairs; soon everybody was running, and a mumble in the fleeing crowd sharpened into the frightening cry, 'The dam has broke!'

Some refugees reached the Country Club, eight miles away; some made only the Park four miles off, where they climbed the trees for safety. Soldiers on lorries went shouting through megaphones: 'The dam has not broken!' But everyone thought they were calling out: 'The dam has now broken!' and the disorder became worse. Shortly, everyone slunk home in the afternoon sunshine, feeling foolish but dry. The artist who observed the Walter Mitty in all of us sensed also the fragility of our widespread doom-laden dams.

### Dreamland

Man has for as long been fascinated at night by the dreams within, as by the stars without, his resting head. Oneiromancy, the divination of the future by dreams, was founded by the Greek Artemidorus, who came from Ephesus on the coast of Asia Minor north of the island of Samos.

Artemidorus lived in Rome between AD 138 and 180, whence he travelled everywhere collecting people's dreams. He wrote five volumes on their interpretation, *Oneirocritica*, still obtainable.

From Artemidorus' treatise evolved the soothsayers' dictionary of dreams, containing such items:

- *Aircraft*  Swift success awaits your ambitions, after overcoming obstacles.
- *Bananas*  Prepare to suffer a minor illness.
- *Church*  Your fondest hopes will shortly be fulfilled.
- *Gun*  Forthcoming dishonour.
- *Nakedness*  You will unwisely employ some attention-seeking device, which may involve you in scandal.
- *Trees*  Forthcoming success and happiness.
- *Umbrella*  Misunderstandings ahead. If it is raining as well, then you will have a friend to protect you.
- *Vase*  If flower-filled, means impending unexpected pleasures.
- *Volcano*  Trouble in store from failure to control your emotions.

In 1899, Sigmund Freud in Vienna published *The Interpretation of Dreams*, which was a flop, selling 350 copies over six years.

Freud redirected dreams from foretelling the future to reflecting the immediate past. Every dream revealed, through its illogical or absurd dramatics, your previous day's unsatisfied desires and lusts. Some of these powerful urges would be strangers to your wakeful mind. Freud decided that most of humanity's nightly programmes were sex shows, though they were unusual compared with these real performances in demanding subtlety for their interpretation.

Freud's dream-book:

- *Aircraft*  The male sex organ, which shares the machines' remarkable characteristic of rising in defiance of the laws of gravity. The first Zeppelin rose in Germany the year after Freud's book, and was soon

sailing sweetly through the dreams of his female patients.
- *Bananas*   Also the male sex organ.
- *Church*   The female sex organ, because it presents a hollowness which the male desires to enter.
- *Gun*   The male sex organ.
- *Nakedness*   The dreamer's sexual notions are bursting to be expressed.
- *Trees*   The male sex organ. This is represented in dreams also by swords, watering-cans, pens and pencils, fountains, snakes, fish and all DIY implements.
- *Umbrella*   Inevitably, the male sex organ.
- *Vase*   Inevitably, the female sex organ. So are ovens, bags, buckets, ships, anything presenting a welcoming cavity, also mussels, oysters and snails.
- *Volcano*   Probably the sex organ, male or female.

The property-list for the Freud dream show is uncharacteristically unimaginative.

After a hundred years Freud has been debunked, but he continues to flow through the world's psychological thought like the zestful strains of 'The Blue Danube'. His interpretation of dreams was no more scientific than Artemidorus'. This is not discreditable. Physiologists know now that dreams occur during those times of night when the eyes suddenly start rapid, roving movements beneath their lids, and when the slow electrical waves of the brain turn quick and jerky. But still nobody knows why we sleep perchance to dream.

## Gambling

Backers make an intense study of a horse's breeding, its form, its track record, the reputation of its owner and trainer, the fame of its jockey, the opinion of the newspapers and how it looks while circling the paddock. But betting on horses has been overwhelmingly proved to be as unpredictable as any game with inanimate numbers. The races would be not much fun otherwise.

We have already observed the human frailty of wanting something for nothing, expressed disastrously in the stock markets. Gambling is seeing into the future, whether for the Derby winner or the next roulette number, but backing your judgment. Unlike the case with other soothsaying, its accuracy is displayed immediately and definitely, and more excitingly. Even the bother of prognostication is spared by lotteries and fruit machines, which produce the future with mechanical efficiency.

Comparatively few people are compulsive gamblers in the way others are compulsive drinkers or eaters or starvers. Dostoevsky in middle age was a bad case:

> He returned, having of course lost everything, and said he wanted to talk to me. He took me on his knee and began to beseech me to give him another five louis. He said he knew that would leave us only seven louis and that we should have nothing to live on; he knew everything, but what was to be done? In no other way could he calm himself; he said that if I did not give him the money he would go off his head,

wrote his second wife, Anna Grigoryevna, of 1868.

'Gambling is the child of avarice, the brother of iniquity, and the father of mischief!' exclaimed George Washington. 'Gambling is the resource only of the bored,' said Jean-Jacques Rousseau, more understandingly. Most gamblers are modest folk laying modest bets to enliven a humdrum life. The betting shop, like the local pub, is a friendly refuge from an indifferent world, where a man can exercise judgment and decisiveness and take bold action in reliably congratulatory or consolatory company. Why be hard on the punter? As everything we do depends on influences outside our control and our knowledge, to live is to gamble.

FIFTEEN

# The Flesh is Weak

Every man has an Achilles prick.

While this book was being put together, a member of the Cabinet, another minister, a Government lawyer and two bishops (one of them RC, hetero, the other C of E, homo) bit the dust of sexual disgrace which has bittered the mouths of so many important persons. Nothing is more delightful for the public to observe than a decline and fall, particularly if the decline is precipitous and the crash spectacular.

Any man whose style of life is fashioned by public esteem must offer in return the small change of respectability. If he dismisses the peril of sexual scandal, this is less that he calculates he is clever enough to get away with it and more that the urge to risk it is irresistible.

Here are four examples.


## Irish Eyes Are Smiling

Charles Stewart Parnell overshadows the murderous muddle of Anglo-Irish neighbourhood politics, in which one side refuses to forget anything and the other refuses to remember.

As the *Dictionary of National Biography* sums him up:

212

His influence on the course of English and Irish history may be estimated by the fact that when he entered public life home-rule for Ireland was viewed by English politicians as a wild impractical dream, while within eleven years he had induced a majority of one of the two great English political parties to treat it as an urgent necessity.

Parnell was born in 1846, in County Wicklow, where his father's family from Cheshire had bought an estate in the days of Charles II. His mother was the daughter of American admiral Charles Stewart, who had fought the British in 1812–14, America's first foreign war, a patriotic landmark. Parnell was an undergraduate at Magdalene, Cambridge, but shunned a degree. In 1874 he became High Sheriff of Wicklow, and the next year he was elected to Westminster, where he perfected the Irish tactics of disrupting the House of Commons.

In 1879, Parnell became president of the Land League, which was founded for the reduction of rack-rent and the transfer of Irish land from the landlords to the people who lived on it. He brought home £70,000 for this from the United States. In 1880, he invented 'boycotting', named after landlord Captain Boycott, the first to be ostracised for taking over the farms of his evicted tenants. The following year, Parnell was sent by Mr Gladstone to jail in Kilmainham (it was tolerably comfortable, grilled turkey for breakfast, chops for lunch, oysters for dinner) for making incendiary speeches. This duly gave him the freedom of Dublin and created him 'the uncrowned king of Ireland'.

He began to tangle with Gladstone's Liberals and the Marquis of Salisbury's Tories. In 1886, after the Bill for an Irish Parliament was thrown out, to be followed by Gladstone's government, Parnell announced that he would in future play by the rules. He preferred 'to win than to force his way' to Irish self-rule. Then things began to go wrong for him. He suffered from rheumatoid arthritis. He spoke infrequently and attended Parliament irregularly. He was accused by *The Times* of conniving at crime and, despite his disavowal at the time, of vindicating and even abetting the Phoenix Park murderers.

A bunch of terrorists had knifed to death Lord Frederick Cavendish, the Irish Secretary, and Thomas Burke, his top Civil Servant, on 6 May 1882. This was four days after Parnell's release from Kilmainham, which had occasioned a torchlight procession in Dublin. The English were duly incited.

Incriminating letters about Parnell and Phoenix Park had been passed to *The Times*. They were forgeries, confected by Richard Pigott, ex-editor of *The Irishman*, a newspaper he had sold to Parnell. Pigott wilted before the investigating commission, vanished to Madrid and shot himself. But the dank peat flung at Parnell stuck. Then, in November 1890, Parnell was woundingly accused of adultery in the divorce suit brought by Captain O'Shea against his wife Kitty.

Kitty O'Shea describes the start of their affair in her autobiography. On a wet and windy day in the autumn of 1880, she had gone for a day trip to Brighton from her home at Wonerish Lodge, in Eltham, south-east London. She had tramped on the Downs, had eaten nothing, was chill and damp. By the platform barrier at Charing Cross – for the train to Eltham & Mottingham on the South East and Chatham Railway via the Dartford Loop – she saw Parnell waiting.

> As our eyes met he turned and walked by my side. He did not speak, and I was too tired to do so, or to wonder at his being there. He helped me into the train and sat down opposite me, and I was too exhausted to care that he saw me wet and dishevelled. There were others in the carriage. I leant back and closed my eyes, and could have slept but that the little flames deep

down in Parnell's eyes kept flickering before mine, though they were closed. I was very cold; and I felt that he took off his coat and tucked it round me, but I would not open my eyes to look at him. He crossed over to the seat next to mine, and, leaning over me to fold the coat more closely round my knees, he whispered, 'I love you, I love you. Oh, my dear, how I love you.' And I slipped my hand into his, and I knew I was not afraid.

They became the Antony and Cleopatra of suburbia.

Kitty O'Shea was six months older than Parnell, the thirteenth and final child of Sir John Page Wood, who had inherited the baronetcy of his father, the Lord Mayor of London. Sir John had been chaplain to George IV's Queen Caroline, and was then vicar of Cressing, north of the Colchester oyster-beds in Essex. The family lived at Rivenhall Place, which had lakes and bridges and park-land and Queen Elizabeth had slept there.

Wonerish Lodge was a two-and-a-half-storey, grey-brick, slate-roofed, tall-chimneyed early Victorian villa, facing south with sun-blinds. It stood in a small bushy garden with a greenhouse, one of a row at North Park, convenient for the shops. Kitty's aunt, Mrs Wood, bought it for her in 1875, also settling on her £3,000 a year in return for Kitty becoming her everyday companion. As Kitty was penniless, and Auntie was sitting on £200,000 and was aged eighty-three, this looked a sound deal.

Auntie lived grandly in Eltham Lodge. Built in 1668, its outside replicating the Maritshuis in The Hague, its rooms were vast, its front hall like a nave, and its walls and ceilings were plastered grandly in blue and white. She had George Meredith come to read to her, at £300 a year. Kitty's husband, Willie O'Shea, insisted that he needed also rooms in London, and Auntie paid for them, too.

Eltham is now SE9, Wonerish Lodge has vanished for

a row of 1930 villas, and Eltham Lodge is the nineteenth hole of the Royal Blackheath Golf Club. Barely two miles away stands suburban Chislehurst Golf Club, its decor buzzing with the Imperial *abeille*, which housed about that time the evicted Napoleon III and Empress Eugénie. The Emperor died there, three days after Queen Victoria's surgeon had brilliantly crushed his enormous eight-year-old bladder-stone. History sinks a long putt.

Parnell and Kitty had met before Charing Cross, that July in Palace Yard, Westminster. She had appeared at the House of Commons demanding to know why he shunned her dinner parties, considerately held not in Eltham but in a Berkeley Square hotel. Parnell was tall, thin, pale, handsome, bushy-browed, bearded, a bachelor. As Kitty entered her departing hansom, a rose fell from her bodice. He picked it from the cobbles, lightly kissing it, and it ended up lying on his heart in his coffin. It was love at first sight.

Kitty was short, plump, wide-mouthed, chestnut-haired and snowy-skinned; a bubbly woman, lively, laughing, clever, talkative, always posing pert questions, the sort that most men sweatingly avoid. The awful Frank Harris, who handled women as masterfully as his contemporary W. G. Grace handled the bowling, found her 'sonsy' (attractively buxom). He noticed at the dinner-table early in their romance that Parnell 'devoured her with his flaming eye, they were lovers and lost in mutual passion'.

Harris found Parnell 'curiously ill-read and ill-informed . . . tall and well-made, but he seemed to me too slight to be very strong; but Mrs O'Shea, whom I questioned on the subject, told me his mere physical strength had astonished her time and again, and she did not dwell on it at all unduly'. He added that 'she exaggerated her Irish brogue with some artistry', which is odd, because she was an Essex girl.

Aged twenty-one, Kitty had married at Brighton Captain Willie O'Shea, in the gloriously frogged uniform of the 18th Hussars. He was fair, moustached, good-looking, glib, gregarious, five years older than she, a 'careless Catholic'. Willie sold his commission and became a banker in Madrid, after that a stud-farm owner in Hertfordshire, and then a bankrupt.

He took work at a Spanish sulphur mine, which kept him away from Eltham for eighteen months. The sulphur was not up to much, the mine went bust, and the London banker who had given him the job was meanwhile having it off with Kitty. The only thing left for Willie was to become a Member of Parliament. In 1880 he was elected by County Clare.

Parnell took an instant dislike to him, but Willie ingratiated himself and became his private secretary for a year, before resigning over Parnell having a common entanglement with a barmaid. Their relationship was already becoming complex.

Parnell was a regular house-guest at Wonerish Lodge, where Kitty had a study built on for him. They took carriage rides to Chislehurst Common, where one autumn Parnell was mobbed by the Irish hoppers come to pick the fields of Kent for the beer of Englishmen. He incited presents from the Irish, including parcels of eggs, which to avoid gullibly poisoning himself he cracked and discarded in the garden, and then fretted that they might poison Grouse, his shaggy Irish retriever.

Willie only once slackened in his hospitality, when he arrived unexpectedly, found the absent Parnell's portmanteau in the guest-room, furiously dispatched it to London and challenged him to a duel in Lille. Nothing came of it, though Parnell had to write pathetically to Kitty, 'Will you kindly ask Captain O'Shea where he left my luggage?'

Willie became seriously stirred over Parnell only in the

summer of 1886, when Parnell's brougham collided with a market-gardener's cart on his way to Wonerish Lodge from Eltham & Mottingham station. It got in the newspapers. The *Pall Mall Gazette* talked about 'Mr Parnell's suburban retreat' and mentioned that he usually resided at Eltham while Parliament sat. As the accident happened after midnight, it appeared a late arrival for an overnight guest, particularly as Captain Willie O'Shea was at the time in Carlsbad.

Willie telegraphed home for an explanation. Kitty wired back that there was nothing to worry about. Parnell said it was all to do with his putting his two horses out to grass for the summer. To avoid further publicity, Parnell took a house to see Kitty in Eastbourne, but the Sussex *Daily News* found out. Kitty dismissed Willie's questioning by reminding him that Parnell's brother lived in Eastbourne, and that she was 'disgusted at your desire and evident attempt to drag my name into a newspaper again'.

Earlier, Parnell had followed Kitty on the train to Brighton on holiday, clipped off his beard at Clapham Junction to avoid recognition (he was tormentingly superstitious) and arrived heavily muffled at his hotel (as Mr Stewart), excusing the wrapping-up with a raging toothache. When the O'Sheas had left Wonerish Lodge for good and moved to a house on the Hove seafront, Parnell avoided three encounters with the unexpected Willie by slipping down the fire-escape and nipping round ten minutes later to ring the doorbell.

Contraception then being a convenience as little used as the telephone, five months before Parnell was sent to Kilmainham he made Kitty pregnant. Kitty used the ruse that somehow escaped the quills of Boccaccio and Chaucer. She passionately invited copulation from her husband in order to shift the blame. Willie became the proud father of a girl, who within weeks wilted and died, a tragedy ascribed to the bad Eltham drains. Kitty's deception usefully kept open the inheritance of Auntie's fortune, which would never have enriched an adulteress.

Willie was broke and sponging on Kitty. Parliament paid him nothing. Parnell had no money, either. In the House of Commons Parnell bought thin cigars and cheap dinners because he had to pay for them; in restaurants he accumulated huge bills because he knew that he never would. Parnell was spending £10,000 a year and he died £50,000 in debt. As fervently as Kitty and Willie, his heart belonged to Auntie.

Willie lost his Clare candidature in the general election of 1885, but was returned in 1886 for Galway through the influence of Parnell. This agitated Parnell's political colleagues, who saw it as a sexual *quid pro quo*. Parnell and Kitty had by then two daughters, Clare and Frances. They looked like their father. Willie accepted them as his. Whether Willie extended the same compliance towards Parnell as Parnell was suspected of offering the Phoenix Park murderers was the hinge of his divorce case.

This came on 15 November 1890. The action was complicated by Kitty accusing Willie of having sex with her sister. A further complication was Auntie having died the year before, aged ninety-seven, leaving her fortune to Kitty but tied away from her husband's hands. Willie furiously contested the will, inspiring the rest of her relations to join in. The will had been made under Kitty's influence, as a favourite and trusted niece. If she could be proved before a divorce judge to have been deceiving her aunt since first moving to Eltham, there was the chance of a probate judge reallocating the spoils. Kitty meanwhile tried to bribe Willie to let her divorce him instead, but failed to raise the £25,000.

Perhaps the divorce had also a political subplot, hatched by Willie and his toadied-to friend the Radical

Joseph Chamberlain, then President of the Board of Trade. No defence was offered in court. No cross-examination was inflicted. Willie won, and the judge described Parnell as a man 'who takes advantage of the hospitality offered him by a husband to debauch the wife'.

It did for Parnell. A king, even an uncrowned one, even an Irish one, cannot survive the ridicule bred of beard-cutting, false names, dodging down fire-escapes and sharing a suburban housewife. He raised laughs for the music-hall comics and inspired a fire-escape toy for Christmas. Gladstone was horrified, though for ten years he had been milking Kitty of Parnell's secrets. The Irish Party turned against Parnell in Parliament, the Roman Catholic Church vilified him, he married Kitty on 25 June 1891 and died in Brighton of lobar pneumonia on 6 October. His favourite book, which he reread without a smile, was *Alice in Wonderland*.

## A Model for Us All

May I again quote Shaw? 'We are an incorrigibly intemperate and ridiculous people in our cups of virtuous indignation.' In 1963, this heady brew killed someone.

The trouble began ten days before Christmas in 1962, when seven shots rang out shortly after lunch in Wimpole Mews. The customary sounds in this district of London were the tap of patella hammer on knee, the puffing of sphygmomanometer bulb and the purr of a consultant's Bentley. A Wimpole, or Harley Street, address is so desirable for the practice of higher medicine that the house numbers sneak round the corners in a string of a, b, c, ds and further alphabetical inclusions. Consultants accumulated in the area in Queen Victoria's day, through its convenience for the main-line termini, permitting

220

patients arriving from the shires to catch the train home in time for tea.

In the hope that such medical magnificence will rub off on them, fringe practitioners pay the painful local rents. Fifty-year-old Stephen Ward of Torquay, son of the Canon of Rochester, called himself 'Dr' but was an osteopath. He had learnt it in Missouri at the college founded by Dr Andrew Taylor Still, who invented it in 1874 from studying the snaffled bodies of buried Red Indians. Osteopaths manipulate bad backs and fiddle with stiff joints and enjoy the patronage of many who are frightened or distrustful of doctors. Some become fashionable: Herbert Barker got a knighthood in 1922, to the outrage of the medical profession.

Shooting at the door of Stephen Ward's flat that afternoon was a West Indian, John Edgecombe, but he had rung the bell first. Inside quivered eighteen-year-old Mandy Rice-Davies, an actress, and twenty-year-old Christine Keeler, a model. 'Model' after this affair took a fresher meaning. Had the ladies removed their clothes and sat impassively for an hour while men stared at them, there would have been no fuss.

Christine Keeler had stopped living with Edgecombe, and it was his way of indicating that he wanted her back. He left in a minicab, but was swiftly arrested and brought to trial on 14 March 1963. Christine Keeler was the pivotal witness, but she had gone to Spain.

The explosive events off Wimpole Street blew open the scandal which has left its debris in the history books.

Back in the summer of 1961, Lord Astor had a house-party at Cliveden, by the Thames north of Windsor, site of the prewar 'Cliveden Set', in which politicians, editors and aristocrats suspectedly remodelled Government policy over the weekends. Enjoying the hospitality was John Profumo, Harold Macmillan's Minister for War, with his wife, the actress Valerie Hobson. Lord Astor had been

221

a patient of Ward's over ten years, and for five years had let him a cottage in the Cliveden grounds at £1 a year.

Ward was having a house-party, too. Guests included nineteen-year-old Christine Keeler, whom he had encountered as a topless showgirl at Murray's Cabaret Club, and Captain Ivanov, who was the Russian Naval Attaché and thus a sharp icicle in the cold war. Profumo met Christine after dinner, by the swimming-pool in the gloaming, he in a dinner-jacket, she in a damp towel. He fancied her and phoned her in London.

MI5 had already taken fright at the Minister for War's chumminess with Ward, the chum of Ivanov. They had a word in his ear. A month later, Profumo, assuming wrongly that MI5 knew all about Christine, prudently wrote her a little note saying: 'Darling . . . won't be able to see you again until some time in September. Blast it. Please take great care of yourself and don't run away. Love, J.'

MI5 was right. Ivanov had asked Christine to enquire from Profumo the date when the Americans were passing atomic warheads to the West Germans. This must have been a difficult topic for a girl to introduce unnoticeably into the conversation in the circumstances.

The face that launched a thousand authorships had already appeared in *Tit-Bits*, when Christine started posing aged fifteen. After the shooting, it became as familiar as the family snaps. The spicy smell of scandal blowing through Westminster appetised the Labour Opposition. George Wigg MP made sly puns about models (later, he had trouble himself with modelling, at Marble Arch). In March 1963, eighteen months after the swimming-pool meeting, Wigg asked in the House that the Home Secretary deny rumours about a member of the Government.

The next day, Profumo made one of those famed, and undebatable, personal statements, Macmillan sitting supportively beside him. Macmillan was already having trouble enough from General de Gaulle, who was vetoing Britain from the Common Market. Profumo said that he had nothing to do with Christine being in Spain instead of in court, which was true, and that there had been nothing between them, which was not.

Truth is a malleable metal in the House of Commons. But to break it is unforgivable professional incompetence.

Ward was being dogged by the police. He complained resentfully to Harold Wilson, Leader of the Opposition, that this was a poor way for the Government to thank him for keeping mum about Christine and Profumo. Parliamentary questions were asked, a Lord Chancellor's inquiry provoked; Fleet Street frolicked. On 2 June, Profumo confessed to his wife in Venice. On 4 June, he wrote to Macmillan: 'In my statement I said that there had been no impropriety in this association. To my very deep regret I have to admit that this was not true, and that I misled you, and my colleagues, and the House,' and he resigned from the Government and from Parliament.

Profumo had considered his association with Christine 'of minor importance only'. He was right. It was politically irrelevant. But it extorted redemption by a life of assiduously performing good works.

Ward was a shifty man who had manipulated for his male patients matters more voluptuous than their joints. He was arrested on three charges of living off immoral earnings, though why anyone should become criminal through his female friends taking in men instead of taking in washing needs thoughtful scrutiny. The crime had been widened in 1961 by a judgment from the House of Lords incriminating the publisher of the *The Ladies Directory*, which afforded the whereabouts of models (illustrated). Ward was charged also with procuring girls 'under the age of twenty-one to have unlawful sexual

223

intercourse with a third person', a generous provision for the age of innocence.

The trial at the Old Bailey on 22 July 1963 stumbled on the slipperiness between promiscuity and prostitution. Prostitution 'is where a woman offers her body for sexual intercourse – that is normal sexual intercourse – or for any act of lewdness for money', prosecuting counsel Mervyn Griffith-Jones helpfully defined. He emphasised that: 'A prostitute is not necessarily the kind of woman that one pictures when one uses that word. It is not necessary for her to ply her trade on the street corner.'

But what difference is there between presenting the lady with hard cash or a diamond necklace? Awkward question.

Christine Keeler gave model evidence and Mandy Rice-Davies gave her reply to Lord Astor's denial of her sexual allegations: 'He would, wouldn't he?', which in knowingness matches Galileo's *Eppur si muove*. Ward was found guilty of living off the earnings of these two frail ones, but by then he was dead in hospital from an overdose of barbiturate.

Suicide, like happiness, originates internally, the cause often tragically trivial. Ward had attempted suicide in 1947 over a woman. Now he was vilified and humiliated over happenings that he, like Profumo, saw as trivial. No one from his smart practice had stood up for him in the witness-box. He was the scapegoat for the public conscience. He had discredited our Government and our governors, and they had wanted him psychologically hanged for it.

The thunderous moral overtones assumed towards something that mattered so little replicated the *Lady Chatterley's Lover* trial three years earlier. In the same courtroom the same prosecutor was then declaring: 'The word "fuck" or "fucking" occurs no less than thirty times. I have added them up, but I do not guarantee that I have added them all up. "Cunt" fourteen times; "balls" thirteen times; "shit" and "arse" six times apiece; "cock" four times; "piss" three times, and so on.'

Such lunatic calculations emphasise that pornography is an item of personal assessment, like constipation. Unlike sin, it varies in place and time. What is vile in England nobody thinks twice about in Holland. The fanciful antics of Fanny Hill were despicably degrading in 1962, but after a court decision were jolly fun in 1963. In 1961, the strip impresario Paul Raymond was fined £5,000 after his now commendably respectable Revuebar in Soho was classified as a disorderly house, and told by the judge:

> Your establishment and others have been vying with each other to see what degree of disgustingness they can introduce to attract members from all classes who are only too ready, out of curiosity or lust, to see the filth portrayed in this establishment. This, I think, is the fourth or fifth case I have had, and this is by far and away the worst.

The outraged condemnation of pornography expresses the human frailty of enjoying a powerful erection of the ego.

Macmillan was shattered by the previously unimaginable Profumo scandal. His party's popularity in the opinion polls trailed Labour by 20.5 per cent, and he trailed himself from the month before at 34 per cent. He seized upon his prostatectomy to resign that October from ill-health, though he lived another twenty-three years, to the age of ninety-two. The other bane of his premiership, General de Gaulle, was also suffering from an enlarged prostate, but he stayed in office and avoided the operation, bypassing his penis with a suprapubic tube into his bladder (I have often wondered if it had a cork stamped *Mis en bouteilles dans nos caves*). The French are mystified at English piousness over sex. Its sanctity was dismissed in the eighteenth century by Chamfort: 'L'amour, tel qu'il existe dans la société, n'est que l'échange de deux fantaisies et le contact de deux épidermes.' ('Love, in present-day society, is just the exchange of two imaginary pictures, and the contact of one epidermis with another.')


### The Unsatisfied Mrs

The monarchical prick generally operates without troubling the British Constitution.

George I and George II toyed tirelessly on the throne with mistresses. Charles II's mistresses made delightfully pretty pictures. Henry VIII, 'a bloody and greasy blot on history', was continually after the ladies-in-waiting. For all we know, King Alfred had one while he burnt the cakes.

Edward VII knew a mistress when he saw one, and his pleasant Edwardian days of mechanical inventiveness, class-melting jollity and moral elasticity, dimmed by the Great War, continued in spirit into the 1930s. Playwright Herbert Farjeon's flapper of 1927, who 'danced with the man, who's danced with a girl, who's danced with the Prince of Wales', cheerfully indicated the Prince's sexual and social attractions. Edward, who was short, slight and youthful-looking, in 1936, at the age of forty-two became the first adult bachelor to ascend the English throne since William Rufus in 1087.

Since the war, Edward's affairs had ripped along with Lady Coke, who was twelve years older than he, then with Liberal MP's wife Freda Ward, and then with Gloria Vanderbilt's twin sister, who had become Lady Furness. It was Gloria who leaked the uppish gossip of the thirties that the Prince suffered from ejaculatio praecox, a mishap fired by anxiety about doing it properly. The psychiatry textbook treatment for this is:

> The woman can be taught how to prolong the love play – she should heighten the man's excitement by temporarily removing the penis or squeezing the base of the glans penis, thus temporarily reducing the erection.

Mrs Wallis Simpson from Baltimore, whose two marriages had lasted a total of twenty years, may have accomplished this.

Mrs Simpson and Prince Edward met in 1931 at a party given by Lady Furness, who was swiftly out in the cold. They were the same age. They became an inviolable couple. They continually graced dinner-parties and house-parties. Wallis was the most hankered-after hostess in England at the Prince's home, the odd Fort Belvedere in Windsor Great Park, another royal folly. She wanted to be the Queen. It would be a social triumph.

To disregard the intensity, and the power upon others, of any woman's ambition was a danger discovered tardily by Macbeth.

On 20 January 1936, King George V died at Sandringham. He was the beloved father of his people, if not of his eldest son. Edward was an instantly popular monarch – resoundingly so a month before his abdication, when he toured the impoverished mining villages of south Wales and declared (unconstitutionally) that 'something should be done'.

On 27 October that year, Wallis was divorced in the impenetrably discrete county town of Ipswich from her husband Ernest, who was the son of an American-born Englishman, the Guards and the Stock Exchange. Divorce was a blot on British public and political life. It excluded you from the Royal Enclosure at Ascot. The Church of

England, of which King Edward was repeatedly reminded that he was the head, was becoming increasingly chilly towards the growing practice of divorce, perhaps to ape Catholic hostility towards the growing practice of contraception.

As Queen Caroline had become an embarrassment to George IV – an adulteress barred from the Abbey door at his coronation in 1821 – Mrs Simpson became one to the British Government.

That summer, the King and Wallis cruised the Adriatic in the chartered steam-yacht *Nahlin*. Their photographs were all over the American papers, but few peeped out in Britain. Until 3 December 1936, the British press perpetrated self-censorship over the relationship, with an efficiency that should have won a raised-arm salute from Dr Goebbels in the Wilhelmsplatz. The cat was transferred from the bag to the pigeons on 1 December by the Bishop of Bradford, Dr Blunt, at a diocesan conference, though he had chided only the King's everyday need for God's grace.

The country wondered what was up. The Prime Minister, Stanley Baldwin, had by then roused himself from his habitual inertia and decided to make a crisis out of it. He had told the King that if he married Mrs Simpson the Cabinet would resign – though why the Cabinet need give its assent like a Victorian maiden's father was another unasked question. On 16 November, the King had told Baldwin: 'I am going to marry Mrs Simpson and I am prepared to go.' They then outlined an outlet: a morganatic marriage, disconnecting the wife and children. But this was invalid in British law, and the Cabinet thought little of it when Baldwin finally let them into all these secrets the day before the newspapers did.

The people massed in dumb expectancy in Whitehall. Demonstrations for the King erupted outside Buckingham Palace. Lord Rothermere's *Daily Mail* and Lord Beaver-

228

brook's *Daily Express* slickly backed him, and Winston Churchill romantically envisaged a 'King's Party' concocted from sixty fervent MPs, but he was shouted down in the House. Sir Oswald Mosley marched his Blackshirts behind the King.

On 10 December Edward abdicated. The next night, he took the destroyer *Fury* from Portsmouth to join Mrs Simpson in Cannes (she had phoned him *en route* from Lyons, advising: 'Don't abdicate, you fool!'). He became the Duke of Windsor. As the *Economist* reflected thirty-five years later: 'The brief reign of Edward VIII demonstrated only one thing; that a constitutional monarch has to quit immediately he falls foul of his prime minister.'

The fuss was soon forgotten. So was the King. The coming of the movies did a disservice to the monarchy. The frail public loves its sparkling heroes, but cannot tell silver from tinsel. Today, princes and princesses are indistinguishable from the actors who appear on television at other times. The actress who plays a princess can go home and do what she likes, but a princess who plays the actress cannot. It is boring for them, as it is for many of the Queen's subjects who have to watch.

After her marriage to Edward on 3 June 1937, which was performed in France by an obscure Church of England vicar, Wallis was irked that the title of HRH was denied her by his brother George VI. But what true difference can it make to any frail human – who, from the tying of the umbilical cord to the tying of the knot on the shroud, undergoes the same joys and sorrows, if in different furnishings – whether they go through life being addressed as 'Your Royal Highness' or as 'Waitress!'?

Mrs Simpson could have seen her ambition fulfilled.

Edward was a fan of Hitler, whom he had visited as Prince of Wales, and who was the couple's first foreign host at his mountain retreat in Berchtesgaden three months after they married. The meeting was all smiles,

**229**

and Edward had twenty minutes' private chat with Hitler, being interested in studying social conditions. The Windsors were later brought unexpectedly home for tea by Goebbels, to his country house at Schwanenwerder, where his wife Magda had to send the gardener hastily to the village for the cakes.

The Foreign Office had needed to keep a watch on Mrs Simpson's contacts with important Nazis. Prince Edward was enthusiastically pro-German: 'You forget I am three-quarters German myself.' The Foreign Office decided to filter the information the Prince received and the opinions he uttered – justly so, it transpires, from Nazi files captured later.

When Europe melted in the hot summer of 1940, the Windsors fled from France to Lisbon. The Nazis still thought so highly of Edward that they wanted to kidnap him. They were frustrated in neutral Portugal, and tried luring him to a shooting-party in Franco's Spain. When a German agent told him that a British defeat was likely he disagreed, but the agent noticed that Wallis 'looked thoughtful'. The British astutely got rid of the Duke by appointing him to govern the Bahamas, where he still corresponded with a Portuguese Nazi go-between.

The Germans did not invade Britain after Dunkirk because they lost the battle in the air, the Fleet was intact at Scapa Flow and the crooked shadow of Nelson was still frightening. But the Chiefs of Staff told Churchill:

> If, with our Navy unable to prevent it, and our Air
> Force gone, Germany attempted an invasion, our coast
> and beach defences could not prevent German tanks
> and infantry getting a firm footing on our shores. In
> the circumstances envisaged above, our land forces
> would be insufficient to deal with a serious invasion.

By the time that German paratroops had landed on the Downs and the Panzers were pushing up from Hastings,

Churchill and George VI would have rightly escaped to Canada to establish a government-in-exile. They would have left behind plenty of 'apologetic statesmen of a compromising kind', from Ko-Ko's little list. The German Embassy before the war, with Ribbentrop the ambassador, had the best parties in London for the best people. And Geoffrey Dawson's *Times* had been as amiable towards Hitler as it became implacable against the King.

For his British Marshal Pétain, Hitler favoured as prime minister Lloyd George, the man who had won the first war and was disregarded and old in the second. Sir Osward Mosley might have been joined in the Cabinet by Sir Samuel Hoare, an appeaser who Churchill quickly extruded as ambassador to Spain, and R. A. Butler, the best prime minister we (luckily) never had. On the throne would be King Edward VIII and Queen Wallis. In the late 1940s, when America had beaten Japan, demolished Germany with A-bombs, and liberated Europe, their fate would be chilling.

The possibility could have been avoided. Had Stanley Baldwin, said Malcolm Muggeridge in *The Thirties*, 'but devoted a quarter of the ingenuity required to unseat his King to unseating Hitler, the decade he largely dominated might have ended less precariously'.


### Gay Abandon

Oscar Wilde is the Queen of male homosexuals.

He was born in Dublin in 1854, the son of Sir William Wilde, who was one of the first ear surgeons, who founded and edited the *Dublin Quarterly Journal of Medical Science*, was the creator of Wilde's incision of the skull and a specialist on Irish crannogs. Sir William had trouble in 1864, when a patient he had treated for a burnt neck accused him of raping her on the consulting couch.

Oscar went to Trinity College, Dublin, then to Magdalen College, Oxford, and did brilliantly (a first in Lit. Hum. and winning the Newdigate). At Oxford, he created his part for the theatre of life: the aesthete, which five years later came in handy for Gilbert and Sullivan in *Patience* ('Though the Philistines may jostle, you will rank as an apostle in the high aesthetic band, If you walk down Piccadilly with a poppy or a lily in your medieval hand . . .'). As a plug for this comic opera, and for himself, Wilde arrived in America to lecture on Aesthetic Philosophy ('I have nothing to declare except my genius').

Oscar Wilde then became editor of *The Woman's World*. *The Picture of Dorian Gray* appeared in Lippincott's Magazine in 1890, and *Lady Windermere's Fan* opened two years later. At St James's Theatre on 14 February 1895 came the first night of *The Importance of Being Earnest* – for writing *that* any man can be forgiven anything.

Ten years before, Wilde had married and set up house in Tite Street, Chelsea, and had two sons, Cyril and Vivian. In 1891 he met 21-year-old poetical Lord Alfred Douglas ('Bosie'). Bosie's father, the Scottish Marquis of Queensberry, had codified the boxing rules, once tried to horsewhip Lord Rosebery the Prime Minister, and was a paranoiac.

Bosie explained later that he and Oscar enjoyed 'familiarities' which would be barely noticed in English public schools (he was at Winchester). But 'of the sin which takes its name from one of the cities of the Plain there was never the slightest question'.

The Marquis could not accept this. On 18 February 1895, he left the misspelt card addressed 'To Oscar Wilde posing as a Somdomite' with the porter at Wilde's club, the Albemarle. The message was lost on the porter, who dutifully put it in an envelope and handed it to Wilde when he next looked in.

The Marquis had already been making a rumpus in Tite Street and in Wilde's other agreeable haunt, the Café Royal. When Oscar and Queensberry had first met there, over the liqueurs Oscar cast a spell of admiring friendship but it swiftly evaporated. Queensberry went round warning London head waiters that if he found Oscar and Bosie enjoying their cuisine he would thrash them both. He wrote to his son, threatening to cut off his cash – for persisting in 'the most loathsome and disgusting relationship' – and to shoot Oscar. Bosie responded with the telegram: 'What a funny little man you are.'

Wilde replied to his own communication by having the Marquis arrested for criminal libel. He would never have stepped on this path to disaster had he that morning gone on a planned visit to France instead of going to the club: but Oscar could not raise £140 for his bill at the Avondale Hotel in Piccadilly, and they refused to release his luggage.

With the energy which Queensberry afforded all his actions, he collected a roomful of young working men with whom Wilde had been sharing sexual activities over the past five years. At the Old Bailey on the morning of 5 April Wilde lost his case, the jury needing merely to whisper among themselves in the box. At 6.30 that evening, two plain-clothes policemen arrested him over his hock and seltzer in Room 53 at the Cadogan Hotel in Kensington, where Bosie was staying.

> We must ask yew tew leave with us quoietly
> For this *is* the Cadogan Hotel,

John Betjeman illuminated the occurrence forty-two years later.

Oscar was charged at the Old Bailey three weeks later

for committing the indecent acts which he had prosecuted the Marquis for suggesting. Ten years before, consenting adult males in private could have got up to whatever they liked, but 'Labby' Labouchère somehow inserted these offences into a Bill for the protection of women and girls and the suppression of brothels. Most of the offences Wilde, stylish to the last, was charged with occurred at the Savoy. One that he was not charged with involved the Solicitor-General's nephew.

After three hours the jury failed to agree. He was released on £5,000 bail, to be back a month later.

Oscar was brilliant in court. His one-liners brought the house down:

> COUNSEL: Did you ever kiss him?
> WILDE: Oh dear, no. He was a peculiarly plain boy. He was, unfortunately, extremely ugly. I pitied him for it.
> COUNSEL: Was that the reason why you did not kiss him?
> WILDE: Oh, Mr Carson, you are pertinently insolent.
>
> COUNSEL: Do you drink champagne yourself?
> WILDE: Yes; iced champagne is a favourite drink of mine – strongly against my doctor's orders.
> COUNSEL: Never mind your doctor's orders, sir.
> WILDE: I never do.
>
> COUNSEL: Have you ever adored a young man madly?
> WILDE: No, not madly; I prefer love – that is a higher form.
> COUNSEL: Never mind that. Let us keep down to the level we are at now.
> WILDE: I have never given adoration to anybody except myself. (*Loud laughter.*)
>
> COUNSEL: Why did you take up with these youths?
> WILDE: I am a lover of youth. (*Laughter.*)
> COUNSEL: So you would prefer puppies to dogs and kittens to cats?

234

WILDE: I think so. I should enjoy, for instance, the society of a beardless, briefless barrister quite as much as that of the most accomplished QC. (*Laughter.*)

COUNSEL: I hope the former, whom I represent in large numbers, will appreciate the compliment. [*Touché!*]

Oscar Wilde was a show-off. So many male homosexuals are. Female ones are generally more introverted. They reflect the puzzlement expressed by a homosexual's wife, Lady Keynes, at a White House dinner: 'Two men – yes – I can see they've got something to take hold of. But two women – that's impossible. You can't have two insides having an affair!'

The third Old Bailey jury went by the plot, not the script and the performance. Oscar Wilde was found guilty. The prostitutes who had gathered in the street outside the court raised up their skirts in joy.

The judge began by congratulating himself:

I hope, at all events, that those who sometimes imagine that a judge is half-hearted in the cause of decency and morality, because he takes care no prejudice shall enter the case, may see that that is consistent at least with the utmost sense of indignation at the horrible charges brought home to both of you. It is no use for me to address you. People who can do these things must be dead to all sense of shame, and one cannot hope to produce any effect upon them.

Wilde got two years' hard labour. It was the severest sentence allowed, and, to the judge's mind, totally inadequate. 'Morality is simply the attitude we adopt toward people whom we personally dislike,' the prisoner had already noticed this widespread human frailty.

# Male and Female Created He Them

Aside from the familiar sexual divisions or cohesions, the increasingly workaday world is becoming increasingly confused about the relations of men and women. Hazlitt got this right in *The Ignorance of the Learned*:

> Women have often more of what is called *good sense* than men. They have fewer pretensions; and judge of objects more from their immediate and involuntary impression on the mind, and, therefore, more truly and naturally. They cannot reason wrong; for they do not reason at all. They do not think or speak by rule; and they have in general more eloquence and wit, as well as sense, on that account. By their wit, sense, and eloquence together, they generally contrive to govern their husbands. Their style, when they write to their friends (not for the booksellers) is better than that of most authors.

Freud in 1933 ascribed feminism to penis envy:

> The wish to get the longed-for penis eventually in spite of everything may contribute to the motives that drive a mature woman to analysis, and what she may reasonably expect from analysis – a capacity, for instance, to carry on an intellectual profession – may often be recognised as a sublimated modification of this repressed wish.

Though feminists have a case:

> One thing that is left over in men from the influence of the Oedipus complex is a certain amount of disparagement in their attitude towards women, whom they regard as being castrated.

The militant woman of this century may resume her place in the home during the next. Our frailties ignite in our enthusiasms, and their ashes look unbelievably odd.

236

Our frailties are the intriguing stuff of history and the essential stuff of literature. We would be boring without them. Our greatest frailty is that our frailties never worry us.

Or is this our greatest strength?

# Bibliography

*Basic Instincts*

McDougall, W. *An outline of psychology.* London: Methuen, 1936.

Mackay, C. *Extraordinary popular delusions and the madness of crowds.* (4th edn.) London: Harrap, 1956.

*Fools and their Money*

Bagehot, W. *Lombard Street.* London: King, 1873.

Brenner, R. *Gambling and speculation.* Cambridge: University Press, 1990.

Galbraith, J. K. *The great crash 1929.* London: Hamish Hamilton, 1955.

Kindleberger, C. P. *Manias, panics, and crashes.* London: Macmillan, 1978.

*All that Glisters*

Holmyard, E. J. *Alchemy.* Harmondsworth: Penguin, 1957.

Quiett, G. C. *Pay dirt.* New York: Appledon-Century, 1936.

Williams, N. *Knaves and fools.* London: Barrie & Rockliff, 1959.

*Ghoulies and Ghosties*

Appleyard, B. *Understanding the present.* London: Pan, 1992.

Starkey, M. L. *The devil in Massachusetts.* London: Hale, 1952.

Summers, M. *The history of witchcraft and demonology*. New York: Knopf, 1926.

Upham, C. E. *Salem witchcraft in outline*. Salem: Salem Press, 1891.


*Long-leggety Beasties*

Anon. *An adventure*. London: Macmillan, 1911.

Condon, E. U. & Gillmor, D. S. *Scientific study of unidentified flying objects*. London: Vision, 1970.

Dingwall, E. J., Goldney, K. M. & Hall, T. H. *The haunting of Borley rectory*. London: Duckworth, 1956.

Ewald, A. C. *Stories from the state papers*. Vol. 2. London: Chatto, 1882.

Frazer, J. G. *The golden bough*. (2nd edn.) London: Macmillan, 1950.

Gordon, R. *Great medical mysteries*. London: Hutchinson, 1984.

Gregory, R. L. *Visual perception*. Oxford: University Press, 1973.

Price, H. *The end of Borley rectory*. London: Harrap, 1946.

Shackley, M. *Wildmen*. London: Thames & Hudson, 1983.

Sturge-Whiting, J. R. *The mystery of Versailles*. London: Rider, 1938.

Thomas, K. *Religion and the decline of magic*. London: Weidenfeld & Nicolson, 1971.

*The Times*, 12 May 1983; 13 April 1992; 1 February 1993.


*Ghouls in Human Shape*

Bertram, J. G. (pseud. Cooper, W. M.) *Flagellation & the flagellants. A history of the rod*. London: Hotten, 1869.

Chapelot, P. *Histoire des faits divers*. Paris: Pont Royal, 1962.

Duff, C. *A handbook on hanging*. London: Cayme Press, 1928.

Thackeray, W. M. *Sketches and travels in London*. London: Smith, Elder, 1899.

*The Times*, 9, 13 May, 22, 26 June, 7 July 1840.

*Cult Figures*

Beckmann, J. *History of inventions & discoveries.* London: BOH, 1846.

Bertram, J. G. (pseud. Cooper, W. M.) *Flagellation & the flagellants. A history of the rod.* London: Hotten, 1869.

Blunt, W. *Tulipomania.* Harmondsworth: Penguin, 1950.

Murray, W. S. *The introduction of the tulip, and the tulipomania.* J. Royal Horticultural Society, 1909/10 Vol. 35.


*Lady Tinglebum*

Burford, E. J. *Wits, wenchers and wantons.* London: Hale, 1986.

Cleland, J. *Fanny Hill or memoirs of a woman of pleasure.* London: Penguin, 1985.

Freud, S. (ed. J. Strachey) *Standard edition of complete psychological works.* Vol. 17 (1917–19). London: Hogarth, 1955.

Gibson, I. *The English vice.* London: Duckworth, 1978.

Mayer-Gross, W., Slater, E. & Roth, M. *Clinical psychiatry.* London: Cassell, 1955.

Ober, W.B. *Bottoms up!* Carbondale: South Illinois University Press, 1987.

Rousseau, J–J. *Confessions.* Harmondsworth: Penguin, 1953.

*The Times*, 12 March 1993.


*Blunting the Edge*

Coffey, T. M. *The long thirst.* London: Hamilton, 1976.

Dingle, A. E. *The campaign for prohibition in Victorian England.* London: Croom Helm, 1980.

Freud, S. *Beyond the pleasure principle.* London: Hogarth, 1950.


*The Last Gasper*

*ASH factsheet*, Nos. 1–18, 1989–92.

Calverley, C. S. *Verses and translations.* (3rd edn.) Cambridge: Deighton, 1865.

Culpeper, N. *Complete herbal and English physician.*
Manchester: Gleave, 1826.
*Sunday Times*, 18 July 1993.
*The Times*, 7 September 1993.
Timbs, J. *Doctors and patients.* Vol. 2. London: Bentley,
1873.


*Sharpening the Scythe*
Berridge, V. & Edwards, G. *Opium and the people.* London:
Allen Lane, 1981.
De Quincey, T. *The confessions of an English opium-eater.*
London: Dent, 1907.
*Drug misuse in Britain*, ISDD, 1991.
Home Office Statistical Bulletin, 19 March 1992.
Jamieson, A. *Global drug trafficking.* London: RISCT, 1990.
Parssinen, T. M. *Secret passions, secret remedies.* Manchester:
University Press, 1983.
Russell, B. *A history of western philosophy.* London: Allen &
Unwin, 1946.
Thornton, E. M. *Freud and cocaine.* London: Blond & Briggs,
1983.
*The Times*, 28 August 1993.


*A Chapter of Accidents*
Hough, R. A. *Admirals in collision.* London: Hamilton, 1959.
Leasor, J. *The millionth chance.* London: Hamilton, 1957.
Lord, W. *A night to remember.* London: Longmans, 1956.
Sabey, B. E. *Road safety in the 80s.* 1983.
*The Times*, 17 September 1830.


*The Future of Mankind*
*BMJ*, 14 August 1993.
Leoni, E. *Nostradamus and his prophecies.* New York: Bell,
1982.
Gibson, W. B. & Gibson, L. R. *The psychic sciences.* London:
Souvenir, 1967.

Parker, D. & Parker, J. *The compleat astrologer*. London: Mitchell Beazley, 1971.

*Selection of casualties for treatment after nuclear attack*: London: BMA, 1988.


## The Spirit is Willing

Chapelot, P. *Histoire des faits divers*. Paris: Pont Royal, 1962.

Hill, D. & Williams, P. *The supernatural*. London: Aldus, 1965.

Newman, O. *Gambling: hazard and reward*. London: Athlone Press, 1972.

Wykes, A. *Gambling*. London: Aldus, 1964.


## The Flesh is Weak

Abels, J. *The Parnell tragedy*. London: Bodley Head, 1966.

Blake, R. *The decline of power 1915–1964*. London: Granada, 1985.

Churchill, W. S. *The second world war*. London: Cassell, 1959.

Freud, S. *The complete psychological works*. Vols. 21, 22. London: Hogarth Press, 1964.

Harris, F. *My life and loves*. New York: Grove, 1963.

Hyde, H. M. (ed.) *The trials of Oscar Wilde*. London: Hodge, 1948.

Irving, C., Hall, R. & Wallington, J. *Scandal '63*. London: Heinemann, 1963.

Kennedy, L. *The trial of Stephen Ward*. London: Gollancz, 1964.

Leighton, I. (ed.) *The aspirin age*. London: Bodley, 1950.

Lyons, F. S. L. *The fall of Parnell*. London: Routledge, 1962.

Meissner, H-O. *Magda Goebbels*. London: Sidgwick & Jackson, 1980.

Mowat, C. L. *Britain between the wars 1918–1940*. London: Methuen, 1955.

O'Shea, K. *Charles Stewart Parnell*. London: Cassell, 1914.

Price, J. H. *A synopsis of psychiatry*. Bristol: Wright, 1982.

Taylor, A. J. P. *English history 1914–1945*. Oxford: Clarendon Press, 1965.

*These Tremendous Years 1919–1938*. London: Daily Express, 1938.

Wallace, I. et al. *The intimate sex lives of famous people*. London: Hutchinson, 1981.